a history of weaponry

THE NEW ILLUSTRATED LIBRARY OF SCIENCE AND INVENTION

a history of ships and seafaring
a history of flight
a history of astronomy
a history of electricity
a history of land transportation
a history of medicine
a history of rockets and space
a history of chemistry
a history of weaponry
a history of communications
a history of the machine
a history of physics
a history of architecture
a history of tourism
a history of occult sciences
a history of archaeological discoveries
a history of advertising
a history of fashion
a history of great building constructions
a history of social progress
a history of money and finance
a history of biology
a history of energy
a history of psychology

Leisure Arts Limited
Publishers, London

COURTLANDT CANBY | a history of weaponry

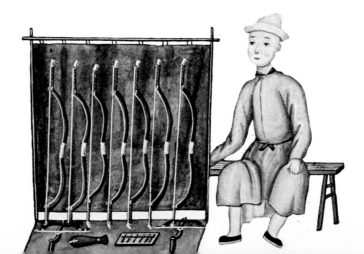

contents

introduction   7

1   *sword, spear, and shield*   9

2   *the horsemen of asia*   23

3   *the knight in armor*   39

4   *the devil's invention*   61

5   *the age of firearms*   75

6   *the balance of terror*   87

chronology   106

credits   111

A history of weapons must necessarily reflect the history of warfare, for throughout the ages weapons have been used primarily in war. Weapons have always intrigued and delighted mankind, and for a very good reason—mankind has always been intrigued by war. In earlier times this fact, so unpalatable to us, was openly recognized. War was a tonic, a test of courage, an outlet for the aggressive spirit of the human male. "It is a joyous thing, is war" wrote Jean de Bueil, who had served under Joan of Arc in the fifteenth century. "You love your comrade so in war. When you see that your quarrel is just and your blood is fighting well, tears rise to your eye... And out of that there arises such a delectation, that he who has not tasted it is not fit to say what a delight it is. Do you think that a man who does that fears death?"

It is worth quoting de Bueil at length to underline the lesson we find in this book about weapons. Man has always loved war and weaponry; and he has loved it so much that he has allowed it to get the better of him. So much science has been lavished upon the development of weapons and so much thought upon the art of war that today we find ourselves in a situation of danger without any precedent whatsoever. The power of destruction at our command is so great that we dare not use it; our weapons are far stronger than we are. During the American Civil War General Sherman once said, "The legitimate object of war is a more perfect peace." Dare we say that of a nuclear war?

No wonder our statesmen and strategists are now thinking in terms of "limited" wars. It is easy to list some of the hazards created by the present nuclear arms race: 1. The danger of an "accidental" war. Irreversible missiles are sent on their way by a false alarm, by the accidental pulling of a switch, by some irrational human behaviour. 2. Levels of armament, too high or too low, invite an enemy attack; but who is to judge the exact level necessary? If your opponent thinks that your armaments are stronger than his, he may suspect you of preparing for a "counterforce" attack to wipe out his weapons systems—and he may strike first. 3. The people are at the mercy of an informed elite who alone know the true situation, but are under close security and thus immune to the force of public opinion. And many times in the past their judgement has proved wrong. Again, who is to judge? 4. Unless something is done soon about the limiting of nuclear armaments, it is only a matter of time before a great many nations in the world achieve the power to make and use nuclear weapons. In this situation, Russia and the United States, now the strongest powers, will be equalled in atomic strength by a number of other powers, and the hazards will be compounded. 5. Some small power with a grudge may, for its own purposes, provoke a "catalytic" nuclear war between the big powers by, for instance, smuggling a nuclear bomb into one of the powers' territory and exploding it. Unlikely, but possible.

It may be appropriate here to quote from President Kennedy's inaugural address, in which he called for a renewed "quest for peace, before the dark powers of destruction unleashed by science engulf all humanity in planned or accidental destruction."

3   *Death of a prehistoric hunter is depicted
in cave painting from Lascaux caverns in France,
one of the earliest showing man in combat.
Hunter's spear leans against bison's side.
Bird is a totem.*

"With a clash of bronze the two armies met, fighting at spear's length, or shield-boss against shield-boss. A tremendous din arose: shouts of exultation, cries of agony, as men killed or were killed; and blood reddened the earth."

Thus the Greeks and the Trojans, in Homer's *Iliad*. By Homer's time war had become almost the natural state of mankind. But it had not always been so. Among primitive hunters and foodgatherers warfare was extremely limited. Many modern primitives, an authority has reported, "find the idea of war incomprehensible." And it has been said of the African Bushmen that "it is not in their nature to fight." Deliberate warfare requires a certain degree of social organization to sustain it, and a rather advanced technology to produce the weapons necessary to massacre the enemy with efficiency. Indeed, civilization and warfare have advanced hand in hand, as we now realize to our cost.

Of prehistoric man we have little left but a handful of bones and a collection of tools, ranging over the millennia from the simplest of chipped pebbles to the finest of worked flints. The bones tell the story of man's gradual evolution from the ancestral primate to *Homo sapiens*; the tools, first used by man-apes in Africa an incredible 1,750,000 years ago, attest to man's unique adaptation to his environment. Being an unspecialized creature, without the canine teeth of the ape, the trunk of the elephant, or the hoof of the horse, man took to the tool to master his environment. In turn, many anthropologists believe, the use of the tool helped to promote man's evolution, confirming him in his upright position with hands

4   Sumerian chariots and spearmen
of world's first organized army
are shown in detail from Standard of Ur,
dating from third millenium B.C.
Soldiers wear cloaks and leather helmets.
5   Mounted Assyrian draws bow
in eighth century B.C. relief from Ninevah.
6   More tolerant Persians inherited
Assyrian culture. Warriors like these
fought against the Greeks at Marathon,
after winning one of ancient
world's largest empires.
7   Gigantic Ramses II of Egypt at Battle
of Kadesh (1286 B.C.)
against warlike Hittites. Ramses
was nearly defeated. Note light chariot.

6   7

free to grasp and manipulate, sharpening his stereoscopic vision, enlarging his already active brain.

Clearly, men have always fought, but these tools provide no evidence of real warfare. Man was always a hunter, and although a club or spear would kill an enemy, its prime purpose was for the chase. But when in the Neolithic period, around 8000 B.C., man discovered new keys to his advancement in the planting of crops and domestication of animals, the situation began to change. Villages were founded, then grew into towns and finally into cities. Wealth and population increased, leading to rivalry over boundaries, property, trade routes. In Sumer (now the lower part of Mesopotamia), where civilization first arose around 3000 B.C, city began to fight with city, the temporary war leader of each city's citizen army eventually consolidating his power and establishing a hereditary kingship, which in turn, for its own ends, built up the military establishment and thus fastened the institution of war upon mankind.

Typical, too, of the coming of civilization was a great spurt in technology, especially in the working of metals, and it was the new technology that supplied the weapons that made organized warfare possible. One can already read about the new weapons in the ancient Sumerian *Epic of Gilgamesh* : "And now they brought to them the weapons, they put in their hands the great swords in their golden scabbards, and the bow and the quiver. Gilgamesh took the axe, he slung the quiver from his shoulder, and the bow of Anshan, and buckled the sword to his belt; and so they were armed and ready for the journey." The sword, the bow, the axe, the spear, these were the principal weapons of warfare for thousands of years. The Sumerian foot soldier of about 2900 B.C. marched in ranks six deep, was armed with a bow and spear, wore a leather helmet, and carried a heavy shield.

Very similar must have been the citizen armies of ancient Egypt, where civilization had arisen close upon that of Sumer. Egypt, isolated by its surrounding deserts, was peaceful until a barbarous people, the Hyksos, conquered it around 2000 B.C. In the process of driving out the Hyksos, Egypt for the first time became militaristic, organizing a national army in two main divisions, north and south; and under Thutmose III carved out the world's first empire in nearby Asia.

Throughout the Mediterranean world the infantry, at first a citizen army, later professional troops, dominated and would dominate warfare up through the Roman Empire, and the weapons were roughly those of the Sumerians. But one entirely new weapon, if one may call it that, was introduced around the time of the Hyksos invasion, the light, horse-drawn chariot. The Sumerians had used chariots, but they were heavy and clumsy, and were drawn by onagers, a type of ass. The horse seems to have come to the Mediterranean with the nomadic Indo-European tribesmen, ancestors of the Persians, Greeks, Romans and Europeans, who had swept down from the north over a period of several centuries after 2000 B.C. Soon the swift, light chariot appeared throughout Western Asia, being introduced to Egypt by the Hyksos, and revolutionized warfare, adding

8   *Famed Greek phalanx of ranked spearmen
is shown on seventh century Corinthian vase.
Equipment of Hoplite included shield,
bronze breastplate, greaves, crested helmet.*

speed as a determining factor in battle. Masters of the horsedrawn chariot were the warlike Hittites, a mountain people of Indo-European origin who briefly created an empire in Asia Minor and Syria. In 1286 B.C., at the famous battle of Kadesh, the Hittites led Ramses II of mighty Egypt into a trap from which he was barely able to extricate himself. Although Ramses went home boasting of a victory, Egypt's power thereafter waned.

In the Aegean at this time a new civilization had grown up. Created by the peaceful, pleasure-loving Cretans, it had been brought to its apogee by the more quarrelsome Myceneans, or Greeks of the mainland, whom Homer later memorialized in his epics. Mycenaean warfare, despite the beauty of Homer's poetry, was primitive, almost devoid of planned maneuvering, strategy, or real leadership. Heroes, rushing into battle in their chariots, opened the combat with spears, rocks, and swords. The infantry, "shield to shield, shoulder to shoulder" then joined the melee, using slings, bows, swords and daggers.

Between 1200 and 1000 B.C. the Mediterranean world fell into chaos. The Mycenaean and Hittite civilizations crumbled before invading hordes. Pirates and raiders attacked cities from Egypt to Syria, (some, called Philistines, settling in Palestine). In the north the Greeks, in a last desperate effort to keep their trade routes open, invested Troy. This prolonged time of troubles was the watershed between the ages of bronze and of iron, for the invaders brought with them tools and weapons of iron, and bronze was no match for the slash of iron blades. When the dust had settled in this time

9

11

10

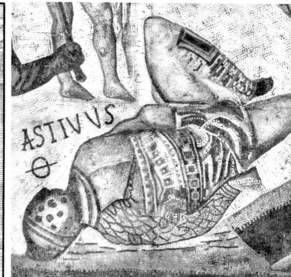

12

9   Roman soldier and barbarian.
History of Roman Empire is dominated
by attempts of legions
to contain barbarian hordes.
10   Romans made a fine art
of both fortifications and siege methods.
11   Two types of Roman battering
rams are used against a city wall.
12   Bloody gladiatorial combats
were staged in every Roman city.
13   Gladiators, armed
in many different ways,
were pitted against each other
or against wild beasts.
14   Roman "tortoise," used to
scale a wall, as shown
in seventeenth century print.
15   Improbable seventeenth century view
of "tortoise" formation in battle.
16   Gladiator raises arms in victory.

13

15

14

16

of change a new power loomed in the East, the Assyrians, who inherited and extended the ancient civilizations of Sumer and Babylon, adding to them a new note of military organization. By the seventh century B.C. the conquering armies of Assyria had swept from the Tigris-Euphrates to the Nile, burning, pillaging, and deporting whole populations at a time, for the Assyrians made a deliberate policy of ferocity. The Assyrians were the greatest warrior people before the Romans, maintaining a highly organized standing army of native bowmen supported by spearmen, with fast chariots as the mobile arm, and cavalry contingents, many from allied or conquered peoples. They made a speciality of siege tactics, employing movable towers with battering rams at the base and archers at the top, to wheel up against a wall.

Most of this technical knowledge and military organization, minus the more ferocious aspects of the Assyrian tactics, was inherited by the Persians, who by the sixth century B.C. had fallen heir to the Assyrian Empire and had extended it until it reached from the borders of India to Egypt and the Aegean. The Persian Empire, by far the largest achieved to that time, embraced most of the civilized peoples of western Asia and the Mediterranean, except for a fringe of troublesome Greek city states across the Aegean from the empire's western frontier in Greek Asia Minor. Darius, first of the great Persian kings, determined to strengthen this weak frontier by conquering the Greeks of Europe. First he organized his empire, dividing it into 20 satrapies, binding it together with a network of roads and posting stations; then

he established his army on a divisional basis, 10,000 men to a division. The core of the army was the infantry, lightly-armed bowmen commanded by Persian or Median officers, but the cavalry, all Persian (as were the 10,000 "Immortals" of the king's bodyguard), was numerous and excellent.

In the Greek city states at this time, the cavalry (except for that of Thessaly) was inferior and the bow was known but little used. The Greek army was democratic, a citizen army of spearmen, each citizen (unlike Homer's day when only the "heroes" were fully equipped) heavily armed at his own expense with cuirass, helmet, greaves, sword and spear. In organization, tactics and strategy the army was again far above the mob-melees of Homer's combatants. These armies, so different, came into collision—notably at Marathon (490 B.C.) and Plataea (479 B.C.)—when Darius, and again his son Xerxes, invaded Greece. The Greek phalanx of heavily-armed hoplites defeated the larger Persian armies of bowmen and cavalry, but the contest was close. Credit is rightly given to the spirit and bold tactics of the Greeks, but as much should be given to the organizational genius of the Persians, notably under Xerxes, who moved an immense army and fleet against Greece, marching the army across the Hellespont on two boat-bridges supported by 674 full-sized vessels.

Greek against Persian, West against East culminated in the creation of a new, Hellenized universal empire by Alexander of Macedon. It was an outsider, Philip of Macedon, who, by force and guile, first united the quarrelsome Greeks and then proposed a war upon Persia

17 Greek fire is used
against an enemy tower.
Illustration comes from
rare tenth century
Byzantine compilation
of older military
treatises by Apollodorus,
Biton, Hieron and
others (see pages 20, 21
and 22 for more).
Byzantines inherited
best of Greek and Roman
military techniques and
used them with effect
against Arabs and
other enemies.
Even Greek fire,
perfected in seventh
century A.D., was
anticipated by cruder
Greek and Roman
"flame throwing"
types of weapons.

18

to the Greek states assembled in congress. After the assassination of Philip in 336 B.C. it was Alexander, his son, who finally conquered the sprawling Persian Empire, first rendering the Persian fleet harmless by methodically reducing all its ports on the Mediterranean, then defeating Darius III in two great battles, at Issus (333 B.C.), and at Gaugamela (in what is now Iraq) in 331 B.C. He then moved eastward as far as Tartary (now in Russia) then southward deep into India until his soldiers, having marched some 17,000 miles, refused to go any further. Returning to Babylon, Alexander died in 323 B.C., in his thirty-third year.

At Gaugamela Alexander's army of 40,000 infantry and 7,000 cavalry faced and defeated a vastly larger army of Persians and their tributary nations, including swarms of cavalry, 200 scythe-bearing chariots, and even some elephants. The backbone of this invincible army, which had been created by Philip, Alexander's father, was still the Greek phalanx, made up of infantrymen armed with an 18-foot pike or *sarissa* and protected by armor and a light shield, whose practice it was to advance in perfect order, presenting a forest of spears. But the older Greek phalanx lacked mobility, a weakness which in the Macedonian army was remedied by the first true use of cavalry, both heavy and light, to protect the infantry and act as its mobile arm. In addition, this excellent army was equipped with light infantry to act as liaison with the faster-moving cavalry, javelin-throwing machines and catapults, and a highly organized staff. Alexander himself had a vision of all peoples at peace under a god-king, which in his short life he did his best to carry out.

His vision finally came to fruition under the long-lived *Pax Romana* of the Roman Empire.

Roman history may be read in terms of the legion. As a citizen army the early legion fought the Punic and Macedonian wars and gained the leadership of the civilized world. As a professional legion, looking to its general rather than to the state, it made the civil wars possible. As an imperial legion it maintained the Empire for some 400 years, and as a decadent legion of barbarians it helped to bring it down. Originally the legion, like the Greek phalanx, was the military unit of a military minded state, and consisted of 3,000 to 4,000 citizens and property-owners arranged in three divisions according to age and experience, the veterans backing up the younger soldiers. Light infantry, and cavalry at the wings, completed it. The legion's weapons were the famous thrusting sword, the javelin (*pilum*), and the light and heavy spear.

It was this legion, well-organized but deficient in cavalry and poorly led by political generals, which was soundly defeated by Hannibal of Carthage at Trebia, Lake Trasimene, and Cannae during the Second Punic War, almost ending Rome's career. Hannibal was a great military genius. His army, made up mostly of mercenaries, was strong in cavalry, which, like Alexander, he knew how to use; and it employed elephants (he brought 37 over the Alps into Italy) to break up the opposing ranks. For 16 years Hannibal ravaged Italy but could not bring the war to a conclusion. What he did do was to teach the Romans how to fight, and how to use cavalry. Scipio Africanus, who eventually defeated him, was a brilliant general

8-19 Various types of
reco-Roman stone-
rowing siege engines.
imilar medieval
ugines were copied
om Byzantine models
uring the crusades or
rect from ancient
oman military
eatises by Vegetius
nd others.

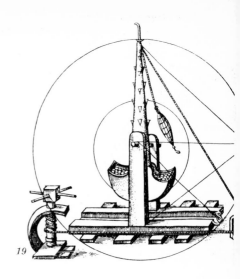

ho raised and trained a Roman cavalry rce which finally overcame Hannibal at Zama 202 B.C.

About 104 B.C. Marius, dropping the property ualification for volunteers, reorganized the gion into ten cohorts of 600 men each -6,000 men in all—with cavalry drawn om foreign rather than native sources. It was is professional legion, with allegiance only its general and its paymaster, that conquered aul under Caesar, and fought the civil wars at ended with the establishment of the mpire. It was a superb fighting instrument, is legion, flexible, confident and disciplined, ained in cavalry as well as infantry tactics, d adept at siege work and fortification. Its mps, both temporary and permanent, were id out in a regular, rectilinear pattern (many esent-day towns were originally Roman forts) d were heavily fortified. Battering rams, ovable towers, missile-firing artillery and tapults were used in siege work against emy fortifications, while artillery more and ore became a part of open warfare. In his mpaign against the Bellovaci in Gaul, Caesar rote, "he marched to the furthest hill, from hich he could, with his engines, shower darts on the thickest of the enemy." Moreover, med camps, trenches, walls and other mporary fortifications began to play as large part in the maneuvering of opposing forces the field as the soldiers themselves.

Under the Empire the highly trained legions the civil wars became the instrument of auto-atic control, being reorganized by Augustus a standing army with sole allegiance to the mperor himself as commander-in-chief. Au-gustus reduced the 60 or so legions, recruited from Roman citizens, to 28, and created another large force of *auxilia* drawn from non-Roman subject peoples, from which came most of the cavalry and archers. Service in the legion was for 20 years, with a retirement bounty in land or money. Augustus also established his own personal army, the élite Praetorian Guard. Soon the legions as well as the Praetorians turned the tables on their chief and began to make and unmake emperors.

Nevertheless, for many long years the legions, posted around the Empire's edges from Scot-land to the Euphrates, managed to hold back the barbarian hordes. A largely defensive policy, however, gradually sapped their vigor and relaxed their discipline until the once-proud legions degenerated into little more than frontier militia and camp garrisons, numerically inferior to the barbarians, lacking a central reserve, and badly trained to deal with the lightning raids of barbarian horsemen. For in a period when mounted troops were becoming the decisive element in battle, the Romans continued to emphasize the infantry. Worst of all was the gradual infiltration of barbarians into the legions themselves. By the late fourth century, for instance, the Roman army was made up almost entirely of Goths. Dominating the army, the barbarians thus dominated the state, leaving little distinction between Roman and non-Roman. It is no wonder that when Rome was sacked by Alaric the Goth in A.D. 410, St. Augustine in Africa, turning his eyes from the ruin of the greatest city of the West, "determined to write a treatise on The City of God."

20 *Dart-shooting catapult,
a schematic view, from tenth century
Byzantine manuscript.*

21 *Byzantine siege engine, after Athenaeus.*

22 *A tortoise for protecting soldiers
attempting to scale wall during a siege.*

23 *A catapult; tenth century
Byzantine illustration
for a military treatise by Biton.*

24 *A siege engine in false perspective.*

25 *A dart-shooting siege machine
called a "scorpion."*

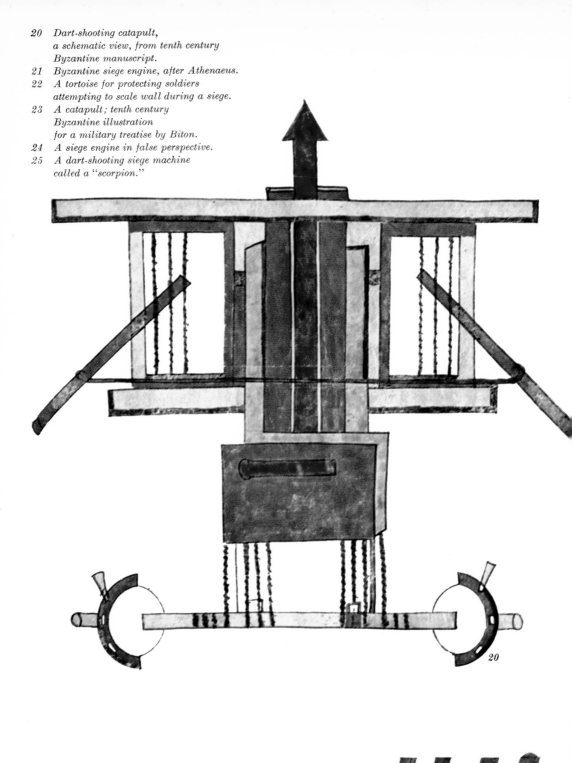

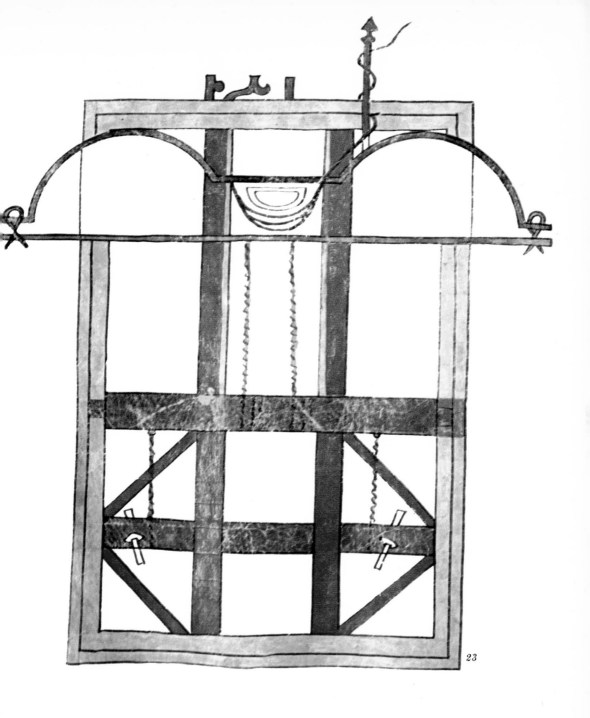

23

24

25

21

26 *Tactical formations of the classical
Greco-Macedonian phalanx, an illustration
from a tenth century Byzantine manuscript.
Byzantine military science, based on classical models,
became a sophisticated art.*

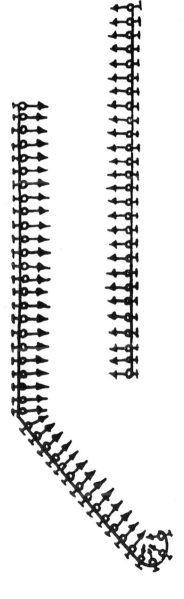

The Battle of Adrianople in 378 B.C., when the Goths under Fridigern defeated the Romans, killing Valens, Emperor of the East, all his principal officers, and 40,000 of his men, was a victory of Gothic cavalry over Roman infantry. "The different companies," reported Ammianus, "became so huddled together that hardly anyone could pull out his sword, or draw back his arm, and because of clouds of dust the heavens could no longer be seen, and echoed with frightful cries. Hence the arrows, whirling death from every side always found their mark with fatal effect... wherever men turned their eyes heaps of slain met them, they trod upon the bodies of the dead without mercy."

For the next thousand years or more after Adrianople the mounted horseman dominated warfare, and the infantry, which had fought the wars from Sumer through the later years of the Roman Empire, practically disappeared. Two factors were responsible for this revolution. In the West an increasing weight of missiles from dart-shooting machines had made it possible to break up the rigid front of the legions, opening them to destruction by cavalry. Even more important was the onslaught from the East of nomad horsemen and bowmen, who became a principal factor in the downfall of the Roman Empire.

Scythian, Goth, Hun, Mongol or Turk, these Asiatic horsemen were much alike. They have often been called wagon folk because they moved restlessly from pasture land to pasture land, the men mounted on their shaggy little horses, the women, children and all their possessions following in lumbering wagons. The horse was their constant companion, the bow

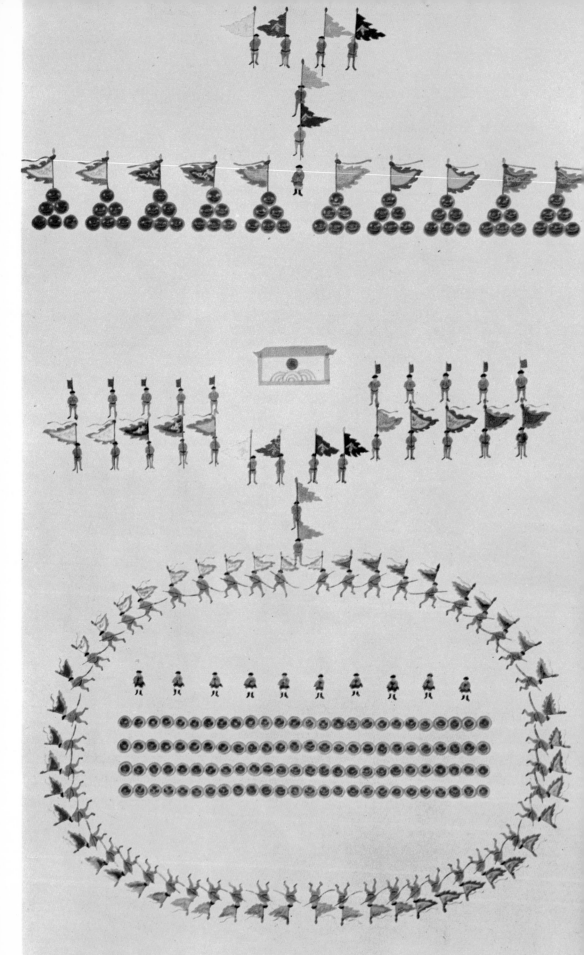

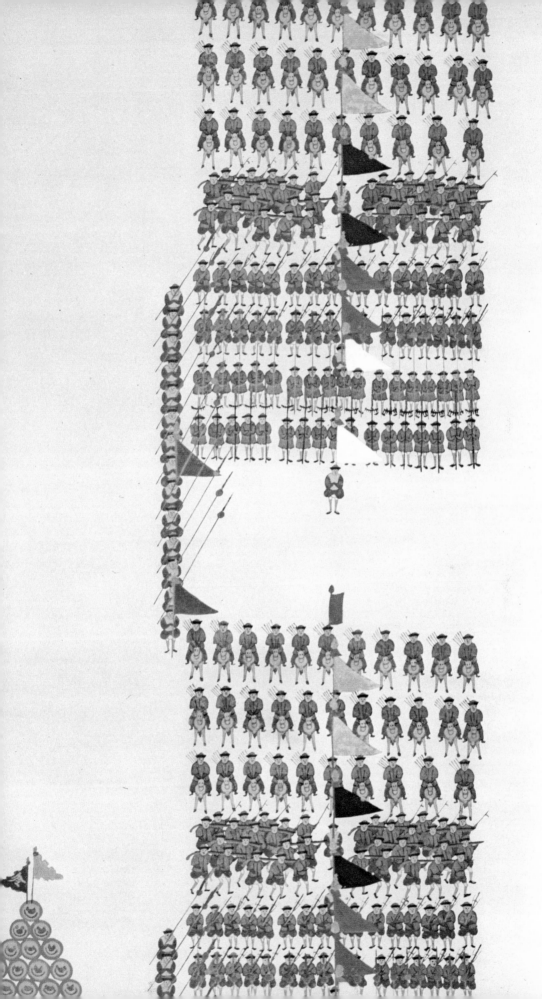

and arrow their favorite weapon, the tent their habitation. They wore light clothing, usually including trousers, and in battle were noted for their hit-and-run tactics and their cruelty. Although raiders and pillagers, they were often virile and disciplined fighters.

From time to time these tribesmen, pushed westward by other nomads or moving in search of new pasture land, burst upon the civilized lands around the Mediterranean (or into China), raiding, burning, looting and sometimes, too, settling down to absorb the elements of civilization. First to appear on the western scene were the Scythians, who from about 700 B.C. to 100 B.C. dominated a restless empire in the grasslands north of the Black Sea. The Goths differed from the other wagon folk in that their bowmen fought on foot while their horsemen were armed only with sword and spear. At Adrianople, however, their vigorous cavalry was decisive, hitting first the Roman flank and then its rear; and when the legions had been broken up, Fridigern launched his infantry from his wagon fort to complete the work. For the Goths, with other nomads, often formed their wagons into defensive fortresses or *laagers*.

The Battle of Adrianople marked the opening of a general infiltration of the Empire by barbarians. Alaric, a Visigothic prince, renewed the Gothic raids and in 410 sacked Rome itself. Vandals swept over Gaul and Spain and into Africa, the Alamanni conquered southern Germany, the Burgundians moved into France, Britain was lost. But the civilizing influence of Rome was still at work and when a new danger threatened from the East some of the Goths, under Theodoric, a king of Gaul, made common cause with the Romans to repel the invader, Attila the Hun. With his Asiatic hordes Attila had swept into France, murdering, burning, and pillaging as he advanced. At Châlons in A.D. 451 he was decisively defeated by Theodoric and Aetius, often called "the last of the Romans," in the final great victory won by imperial Rome in the West.

Even today Hun is a synonym for savagery. Skilled bowmen mounted on small, swift horses, the Huns first moved westward from the steppes of Asia in the fourth century A.D. Even the Goths, barbarians themselves, considered them a "savage race," the offspring of sorceresses and unclean spirits. "They made their foes flee in horror," wrote a contemporary, "because their swarthy aspect was fearful, and they had, if I may call it so, a sort of shapeless lump, not a head, with pinholes rather than eyes. Their hardihood is evident in their wild appearance... They are short in stature, quick in bodily movement, alert horsemen, broad shoulders, ready in the use of bow and arrow, and... they have the cruelty of wild beasts." In warfare the Huns depended upon mobility, surprise, cunning and terror, falling back upon their defensive *laager* when necessary. They could not stand up to a determined attack and were unable to storm fortresses or walled cities. "Almost glued to their horses," they ate, drank, conferred and even slept on horseback. In close combat they took to swords, often lassoing their enemies to render them helpless.

Attila briefly threatened Italy after his defeat at Châlons, but after his death his loosely

35

organized empire fell to pieces and the Huns, as a people, soon disappeared from Europe. The Goths, however, went on to conquer Italy under another Theodoric, often called "the Great," who initiated a revival of western Roman culture which might well have changed the course of history had not Justinian, Emperor of the East, determined to reconquer the West. In a series of campaigns he seized Africa from the Vandals and Italy from the Goths and in so doing so devastated and impoverished the West that soon afterwards it sank irrevocably into the Dark Ages.

Belisarius and Narses, Justinian's generals in Italy, had taken full advantage of the superiority of their mounted bowmen over the foot archers of the Goths; for by this time most armies, whether barbarian or Roman, depended primarily upon cavalry. Heavy armored cavalry, copied from those of the Sassanian Persians, successors to the Parthians, had been introduced into the eastern Roman army as early as A.D. 351. Over 200 years later, after the military reforms of the Emperor Maurice, the heavy trooper, armed - with sword, dagger. bow and lance, had emerged as the elite core of the Byzantine army. Helmeted in steel with a nodding crest, clad in a long shirt of mail with a surcoat, gauntleted and shod in steel, prancing on a charger protected by frontal armor, and with a long pennant bearing the device of his unit streaming from his lance, the Byzantine trooper must have been a stirring sight—a curious prefiguring of the medieval knight. The light trooper was less heavily armed and armored while the infantry played a definitely subordinate role.

After Maurice's reforms in the sixth century the Byzantine army, little changed, held off Persian, Slav and Saracen for almost 500 years for it was superbly organized and made up in efficiency for what it lacked in numbers. The regular troops underwent an intensive training and were subject to a rigid discipline. "Few men are naturally courageous," wrote Maurice "but training and exercises make them into good soldiers." To the Byzantine, war was a science. Strategy and tactics were intensively studied, while the order of battle provided that series of reserve shocks that makes for victory in cavalry combat. Finally, the army was backed up by an elaborate arsenal of siege and artillery engines.

The most wily and dangerous enemy the Byzantines had to face were the Saracens, who had poured out of the Arabian desert in the seventh century to conquer an empire which stretched from the borders of China to those of France. But the prize of Constantinople besieged in the seventh and again in the eighth century, was denied them by the strength of its walls, the ingenuity of Byzantine engineers and the efficiency of the army and fleet. For centuries thereafter the Byzantine army repulsed sporadic Saracen raids into Asia Minor so successfully that the Saracens, whose sole advantage lay in numbers, speed of attack and fervor, adopted their enemy's arms and military practices wholesale. But they still could not stand up to the Byzantines: "Horse for horse and man for man," wrote Leo the Wise, "the Byzantines were heavier, and could ride the Orientals down when the final shock came." At the other end of their empire the

36

aracens met another check when a Moslem-
oorish horde of horsemen, raiding deep into
rance, was defeated by the Frankish leader,
harles Martel, at Tours in 732. The victory has
ten been trumpeted as the saving of the
est, though the Moslems seem to have been
ostly intent upon plunder rather than
nquest. Nevertheless, Tours did stop the
aracen advance, and helped to establish the
ranks as overlords of France.

At this time and for centuries earlier the
ranks and their Germanic kinsmen the Saxons,
nlike most other nations, depended upon
fantry rather than cavalry in battle, though
y the time of Charlemagne even the Franks
ad taken to the horse. The early Franks, fierce
arriors with blond or red hair and flowing
ustaches, used the sword, dagger, bow and
e *framea* or lance, but their great weapon was
e *francisca* or carefully-weighted throwing axe
hich they hurled at the enemy with deadly
ccuracy. The Vikings were essentially sea
iders and lived with their ships as the Huns
d with their horses. Their lightning raids on
nd were made with the aid of horses seized for
e occasion; yet on the whole they too fought
infantry, using the great battle axe which
uld lop off the head of a horse at one stroke.
iking or Scandinavian mercenaries, armed
ith the axe, served with the Byzantines in
creasing numbers during the tenth and
eventh centuries, the famous Varangian Guard
eing formed in 988.

The period of Byzantine greatness was ended
y another group of wagon people, or Asiatic
orsemen, at the battle of Manzikert in A.D. 1071.
he Seljuk Turks, named for their original,

half-legendary leader, came from the steppes
of Central Asia. In time they began to raid
deep into Armenia and Asia Minor, the principal source of Byzantine armies and revenues.
The Empire rallied to the defence of its lands
under the Emperor Romanus Diogenes, a fine
but over-impetuous general, who marched
against the Seljuk Alp Arslan with a motley
army of mercenaries and allied nations, including other Turks and Normans. At Manzikert
he was defeated and captured (Alp Arslan
magnanimously released him for a ransom),
opening the whole of Asia Minor to gradual
infiltration by the Turks. Although the Byzantine Empire lasted until 1453, it never recovered from the loss of Asia Minor to the Seljuks.
The weakening of this western bastion against
the Moslem helped to bring on the First
Crusade a few years later.

The depredations of the Huns and Turks were
but curtain-raisers to those of the Mongols,
greatest of the wagon folk, whose disciplined
armies overran a great part of the world in
the thirteenth century, from Russia and Syria
to the coasts of China. In A.D. 1258, for instance,
while Hulagu Khan was besieging Baghdad,
another Mongol army from China was pillaging
Hanoi in Indo-China. When Hulagu, moving
westward towards Egypt after the destruction
of Baghdad, was defeated on the ancient plain
of Esdraelon (the Biblical Armageddon), he
had in his artillery train a large corps of Chinese
engineers to work the mangonels and the
machines which discharged three huge naphtha-
tipped "fire arrows" at once. In China a few
years later Hulagu's brother, Kublai Khan,
prevented from reaching the sea by two

stubborn cities on the Han, called in Mesopotamian engineers and siege machines to reduce their walls.

The Mongol empire was truly an international one. Although as nomads the Mongols delighted in destroying cities with the utmost brutality, they employed terror as a deliberate tactic. They were barbarians but by no means savages. Genghis Khan, founder of the empire, who came to power in 1206, was a military genius who knew the value of discipline, organization, and technology. Although illiterate, he set up a civil administration staffed by literate clerks from subject nations, encouraged commerce, maintained highly efficient communications throughout his empire and employed engineers, craftsmen, and skilled artisans of all types to turn out vast quantities of arms and the latest types of artillery.

As a result the Mongol army was for many years the best trained, best disciplined, and best equipped in the world. As Genghis formed it, the army depended upon mobility, discipline, and firepower for its success, and he used it with superb skill. He destroyed the Persian empire in a short five months. Being Asian, it was a mounted army, divided into light and heavy troopers which because of their rigorous training and discipline could be moved about with lightning speed and in perfect order, following commands given by signal flags, or by lanterns at night, or even by means of whistling arrows. Light troopers first harassed the enemy with a murderous barrage of arrows under which, according to one chronicler, they "fell to the right and left like the leaves of winter." The Mongols never closed until the enemy had been weakened and disorganized by their fire; then the heavy troopers, armored in plates of lacquered hide and armed with lance and saber, charged in for the decisive blow. This was an almost perfect combination of fire and shock tactics. Moreover, the army's firepower was augmented by portable artillery, and its troops could endure incredibly long and rapid marches. The armies, exploits, and empire of Timur the Lame (Tamerlane) of Samarkand in the fourteenth century were patterned closely after those of the Mongols. Although he overran India, his conquests were on a somewhat more restricted scale.

The Mongols, however, tried to conquer the known world. Mongol armies overran the plains of Poland and Hungary, defeating the Poles at Wahlstatt in 1241, and might have moved on into Europe had not the great Khan died in Asia, necessitating the withdrawal of the troops. About 1256 Hulagu and Kublai, grandsons of Genghis Khan, set out east and west. Hulagu marched on Baghdad, the teeming, cultivated metropolis of Islam. When the Caliph Mustasim made a show of resistance the Mongols swarmed into the city, killing, looting, and burning for 17 days, leaving its streets piled high with corpses. Some say 100,000, others 800,000 inhabitants perished, while the hapless Caliph was rolled up in a carpet, to avoid spilling his royal blood, and trampled to death by horsemen. For his part Kublai Khan overran China and set himself up as emperor. From China, the Mongols absorbed much of military value, for the Chinese, while not warlike, displayed a passion for the art and science of war, and had early developed

laborate tactics, siegecraft, and the use of war engines to a high point of intellectual refinement. Their besetting weakness was a predilection for the defensive, already shown in the building of the Great Wall in the third century B.C. But the result of Chinese craft added to Mongol vigor was a war machine such as the world had never seen.

The Mongols, as it happened, did not conquer the world. Hulagu was turned back from Egypt, Kublai from Japan. There were two abortive invasions of Japan, in 1274 and 1281, both frustrated not only by storms and ill-luck but by the formidable samurai, or warrior class of Japan. During the first invasion, it is said, when a single samurai would advance like a Homeric hero to challenge the enemy to combat, the disciplined Mongol ranks would open up to let him pass, then silently close in around him and cut him to pieces.

The contrast is instructive, for the Japanese glorification of the individual warrior, so different from the Mongol teamwork, dated from very early times and was strictly a native tradition. Japan borrowed most of the rest of its culture from China, but it was undoubtedly its long isolation from the rest of the world that preserved, until very recent times, the feudal ideal of the warrior. Not until the close of the seventeenth century did the Japanese begin to realize the value of concentrated movements of attack. Pitched battles between early samurai, opened by a singing arrow and shouts, boasts, and challenges on either side, resembled a gigantic, formalized fencing match. The samurai, weighted down with gorgeous armor, gold or silverplated and tied together with many-colored cords of silk or leather, was a master of the bow and the sword—the long sword, sometimes five feet long, for fighting, and the short sword for beheading the fallen foe or for committing suicide (for hara-kiri was a part of his code.) Swords made by the master craftsmen of Japan have seldom been surpassed.

Already by the Kamakura feudal period (A.D. 1185-1333) the warrior class and their military cult, compounded of Zen Buddhism, Spartan endurance, loyalty, and worship of the sword as a symbol of rights and status, had begun to dominate Japanese life. Even monks, like medieval Templars, turned their monasteries into fortresses and happily waged war. In the sixteenth and seventeenth centuries, as the warrior class began to lose power, their military cult was exalted into a national code called Bushido, which combined the aesthetic and mystical aspects of Zen and Shintoism with the strict military code of the warrior—a combination which was to become one of the chief characteristics of the Japanese people. "As among flowers the cherry is queen, so among men the samurai is lord" was a favorite saying.

Feudalism in Japan took long to die. The last remnants were only abolished at the Meiji restoration in 1870. The symbolic end came five years later, when the wearing of swords was prohibited. In Europe feudalism disappeared far earlier; yet there are interesting comparisons between the knight and the samurai, Bushido and the western code of chivalry.

38   *The last of armor. A seventeenth century
swordsman takes a defensive position.
The culmination of the mounted knight
in full plate armor came in the late fifteenth
and early sixteenth centuries. By the seventeenth
century firearms and artillery had reduced armor
to the remnant shown above.*

"No land without a lord, no lord without land." This was the essence of feudalism. Property and sovereignty were confused, and no wonder, for after the breakdown of Charlemagne's empire no state in Europe had either the power or the wealth to offer protection against marauding Vikings, Hungarians, or Saracens —nor for that matter against the raids of neighboring chieftains. In the dark ages the local lord with his stronghold and his armed retainers or knights became the unit of security. In turn he "commended" himself for protection to the local count or duke, who in exchange for certain obligations, chiefly military, left him in sole control of his land or fief. Thus by the early Middle Ages Europe was broken up into innumerable little fiefs, each with its castle and lord, all of them loosely bound together through the system of feudal give-and-take into larger units which were practically little kingdoms in themselves.

The last stand of western infantry against feudal cavalry was at Hastings in 1066, when the magnificent shield wall of Harold of England withstood charge after charge of the Norman knights until at nightfall it was finally broken up, and Harold and his brave housecarls went down fighting to the last. Thereafter for three hundred years or more the knight dominated western warfare. A lumbering half-ton fighting machine encased in sixty to seventy pounds of steel, mounted on a massive charger, his heavy lance at rest, his great two-handed sword at his side, his squires hovering at his back, the knight, in the full flush of the Middle Ages, must have been a magnificent spectacle. But he was also an expensive investment, and since land was wealth, only the landed aristocrat could afford to arm himself in steel from head to toe besides maintaining a private army of vassal knights. Each vassal, paying "liege homage" to his lord, agreed to follow him into battle with his own knights for forty to sixty days. He agreed also to defend his lord's life and honor, go into captivity in his place, help to ransom him if necessary, pay an "aid" when his eldest son was knighted or daughter wed and a host of other obligations. But in turn the vassal was confirmed in the lordship of his fief.

The knight was a fierce fighter but a poor soldier. Moreover he was dangerously proud, despising all footmen and any weapons but his own. "Encased as he was in iron, looking down upon life from the vantage point of horseback," Lynn Montross has written, "he naturally tended to develop an arrogance out of all proportion to his military worth." There was no semblance of a hierarchy of command in the medieval army, since command was based on social status rather than competence. Nor was there any conception of strategy or tactics. Grouped in loose "battles," knights rushed enthusiastically into combat then took to individual duels about the field, hoping to capture an opponent for ransom. There were few big battles, most being minor raids or skirmishes. Armies were small (only about three thousand knights went on the First Crusade), seldom operated far from base, and spent interminable months besieging castles—or rather starving them out, for siege methods were primitive and castles abundant. The infantry, indifferently armed and unorganized, was unimportant and was employed chiefly in menial duties and in siege work. Finally, warfare was limited not only by its primitive nature but by the church's active disapproval of excesses—and the Middle Ages at least displayed a certain moral unity.

The strengths and weaknesses of the feudal armies of Europe were revealed during the crusades. "All Christendom is disgraced by the triumphs and supremacy of the Moslems in the East" declared Pope Urban II at the Council of Clermont in 1095. "Christian kings should therefore turn their weapons against these enemies of God, in place of warring with one another as they do. They ought to rescue the Holy Land and the Holy City . . ." The preaching of the First Crusade was so successful, especially in France, where it took on the aspect of a national movement, that by 1097 a heterogeneous army had assembled at Constantinople. Two years later Jerusalem was stormed and its inhabitants massacred with indescribable brutality, after which "rejoicing and weeping from extreme joy" the crusaders flocked to the Holy Sepulchre to worship.

Described by an Arab opponent as "animals possessing the virtues of courage and fighting, but nothing else," the crusaders were militarily superior to the Moslems only in their armor and in their military impetuosity—unless perhaps one counts their possession of the crossbow or arbalest, one of the few great military inventions of the Middle Ages, which began to appear during the crusades. Clumsy to wind up, the arbalest was nevertheless so powerful a weapon that the church in 1139 forbade its use, except against the infidel, "as a weapon

39 Child's plate armor, intricately ornamented, of the late "decadent" period of the sixteenth century. By this time armor had become a ceremonial costume rather than a device to protect a soldier in war.

40   41   42   43   44   45   46   47

40 Battle-axe, early sixteenth century.
41 War scythe, a very primitive weapon.
42 Partisan, an early type of halberd.
43 A Swiss Vouge, a shafted weapon dating
   from the beginning of the fifteenth century.
44 A fork, about 1600, half tool half weapon.
45 A Morgenstern (Morning Star), sixteenth century,
   a typical peasant weapon.
46 German halberd of the sixteenth century.
47 A Sackbut, a word derived from the
   French saquer, pull, bouter, to thrust.
48 Late sixteenth century German halberd.
49 Lucerne hammer, sixteenth century.
50 A French watchman's Vouge, about 1450.
51 German battle-axe, sixteenth century.
52 A sixteenth century Guisarme, derived from
   the woodcutter's billhook.
53 German battle-axe of the fifteenth century.
54 A fifteenth century Swiss halberd of the
   Zurich type—the classic Swiss weapon.

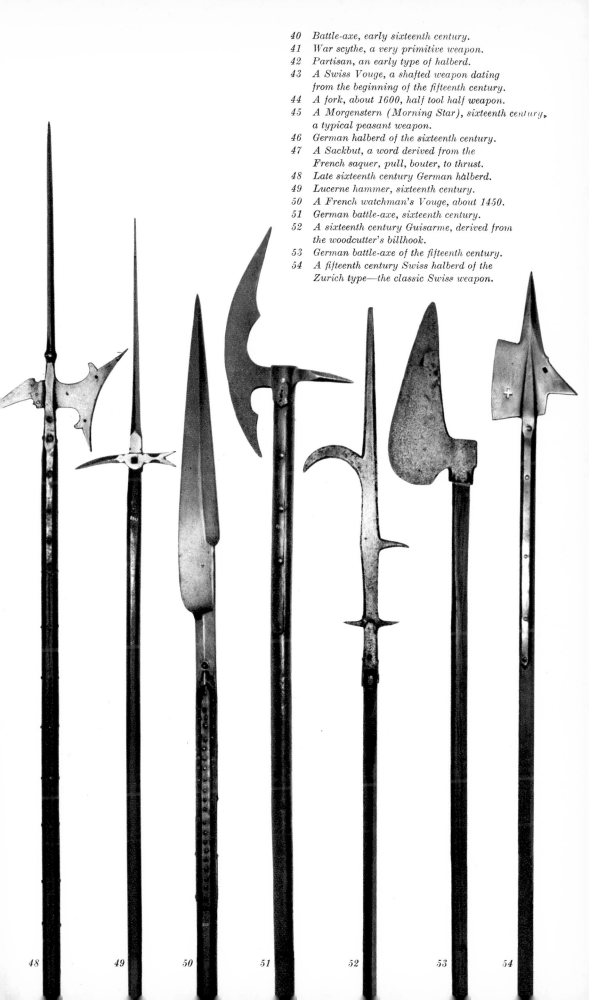

55   58

59 56   57   60 61 62

55   A "Cinquedea" dagger, Ferrara type.
56   "Gothic" battle-axe, late fifteenth century.
57   German two-handed sword, sixteenth century.
58   Late sixteenth century Swiss dagger.
59   Flail and chain, sixteenth century.
60   Ornamented sword, Italian, sixteenth century.
61   Swiss saber, late sixteenth century.
62   Sword of justice, Swiss.
63   A knight's ceremonial mace sixteenth century.
64   Horseman's sword, eighteenth century.
65   Stiletto of the seventeenth century.
66   Two-handed sword, sixteenth century.
67   Cavalryman's war-hammer, sixteenth century.
68   Sword of the end of the sixteenth century.
69   Dagger for left hand, seventeenth century.
70   War-flail, sixteenth century.
71   A ceremonial mace.
72   Sword, about 1550, with a wide guard.
73   Dagger of the end of the sixteenth century.
74   Sixteenth century Italian sword made by Caino.

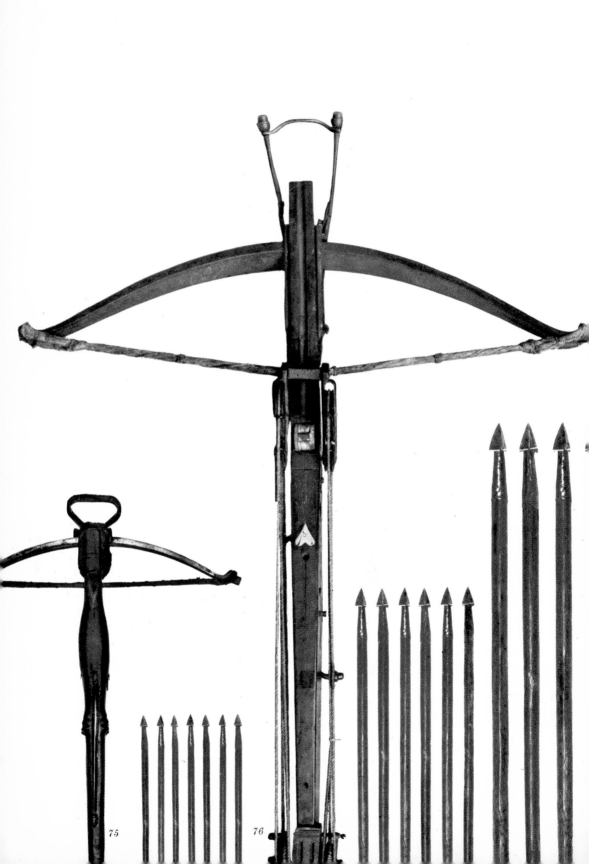

75   76

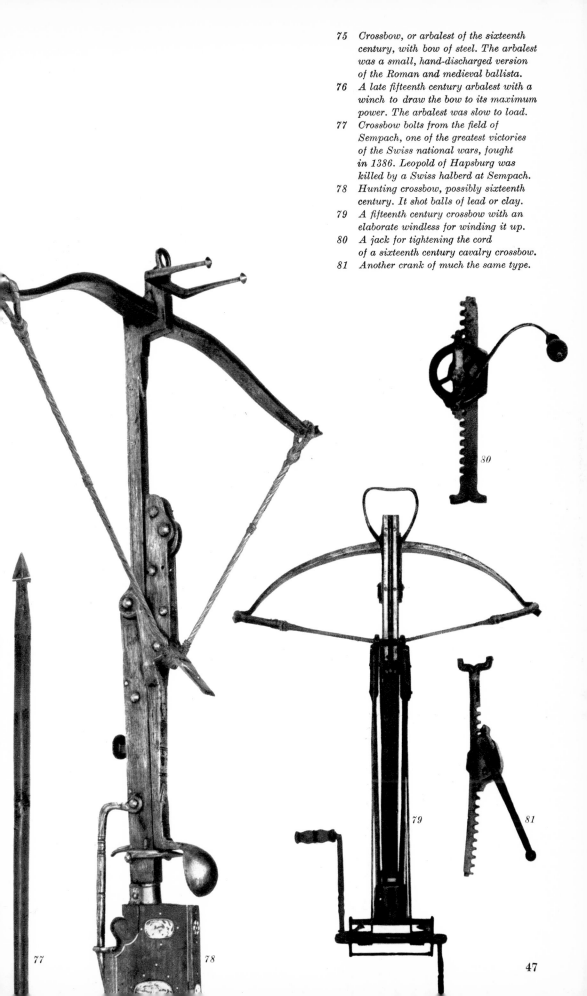

75 Crossbow, or arbalest of the sixteenth century, with bow of steel. The arbalest was a small, hand-discharged version of the Roman and medieval ballista.

76 A late fifteenth century arbalest with a winch to draw the bow to its maximum power. The arbalest was slow to load.

77 Crossbow bolts from the field of Sempach, one of the greatest victories of the Swiss national wars, fought in 1386. Leopold of Hapsburg was killed by a Swiss halberd at Sempach.

78 Hunting crossbow, possibly sixteenth century. It shot balls of lead or clay.

79 A fifteenth century crossbow with an elaborate windless for winding it up.

80 A jack for tightening the cord of a sixteenth century cavalry crossbow.

81 Another crank of much the same type.

hateful to God and unfit for Christians." Shades of disarmament! The crusaders, like the troopers of Byzantium, were easily able to ride down their opponents if their first massive charge succeeded; but the Moslems soon learned to deny them this favor by avoiding pitched battles. The Battle of Hattin is the best example. In 1187 the great commander Saladin, who had united the Arab world against the invaders, lured the massed armies of the crusaders into the waterless wastes near the Sea of Gallilee. There, crazed by thirst, huddling about their revered standard, the True Cross, the crusaders were demoralized and decimated by the arrows of the enemy without ever really coming to combat.

The strength of the invaders lay rather in their defensive system of magnificent castles, supplied from the sea by their maritime allies, the Venetians and Genoese—a system which was able to maintain the Frankish states of Syria and Palestine for almost two hundred years. The crusaders never actually conquered or settled the land but merely occupied parts of it. The mainstay of their armies were the religious orders of knights, the proud and quarrelsome Templars and Hospitallers, professional soldiers who were supplemented by the usual feudal levys and by native mercenaries, many of whom were "turcopoles," or renegade Moslems.

Curiously enough, two hundred years of crusading had little military effect upon the West, except in the art of fortification, which was strongly influenced by Byzantine and Arab military architecture. Richard of England, for instance, on his return from the crusades, built in France in 1197 his formidable Château Gaillard, which, with its rounded keeps and concentric walls became the military key to Normandy.

The feudal knight learned practically nothing from the crusades; but the interchange of goods and ideas between East and West helped to create a new Europe in which he soon found himself an anachronism. If castles proliferated, so did the towns with their flourishing trade, their merchant class, their crafts, guilds, markets and citizen militia. War, too, grew commercialized, as standing armies and mercenary troops began to replace the feudal levy and its unsatisfactorily short, forty-day service. Many a man-at-arms, clad now in plate armor and thus more than ever an expensive item, found he could sell his services and thus turned mercenary, replacing loyalty to his lord with loyalty to the highest bidder. And the highest bidder was often the king, who found the mercenary a better prop to his power than the fractious vassal.

The feudal system was thus undermined, and so was the military system represented by the knight, as his helter-skelter charges began to run into organized opposition. At Courtrai in 1302 the French nobles, charging into a marsh, were slaughtered by the despised citizen militia of Flanders. In 1311 the proud French knights of the Duke of Athens, lured into another swamp in Greece by the mercenary infantry of the Catalan Grand Company, perished almost to a man. These disasters were straws in the wind. When, later in the century, Swiss pikemen and English longbowmen began to inflict defeat after defeat upon the proud chivalry of Europe, it became evident that the days of the knight were numbered. The infantry, after a thousand years of neglect, was again coming into its own.

By the fourteenth century the English longbow, adopted from the Welsh, had become a most efficient weapon. In the hands of the well-trained yeoman its accuracy, at the standard practice range of two hundred and twenty yards, was frightening, and it could carry twice as far with effect. First used against the Scotch, its great triumph, as all the world knows, came at Crécy in 1346, when it proved its power over the massed chivalry of France. "For the bowmen let fly among them at large" a contemporary wrote, "and did not lose a single shaft, for every arrow told on horse or man, piercing head, or arm, or leg among the riders and sending the horses mad." After Agincourt in 1415 the longbow began to decline in importance.

In their great period the Swiss columns were irresistible. From Laupen in 1339 to Dornach in 1499, fanatically patriotic, courageous, and determined, they repelled every attack upon their cherished mountain home. In actual fact they always attacked first, moving into battle with startling rapidity and cohesion, usually advancing in an echelon of three divisions well separated for ease of maneuver. Each column, wearing a minimum of armor to increase mobility, presented a moving forest of spears, 18-feet long with steel heads, those of the first four ranks projecting forward, the rest held upright in reserve amidst a panoply of banners. While crossbowmen skirmished in front, "the solid masses" as Sir Charles Oman writes,

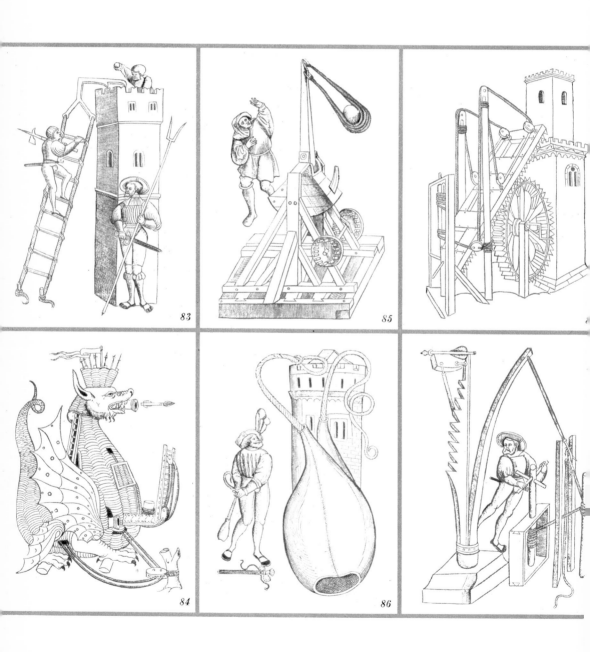

83

85

84

86

83 Much ingenuity
was expended in designing
late medieval siege engines.
Here is an assault ladder.

84 Fantastic siege engine. Early
cannon did shoot pointed bolts.

85 A sling-shot catapult.

86 Soldier with sling-shot
and an enlargement of the device.

87 Gear-operated assault bridge.

88 A "scorpion" shooting a bolt.

89 A mobile assault bridge.

90 Cannon on turntable-tower.

91 An early attempt
at an "armored car."

92 Method of constructing
palisades to protect siege cannon.

93 Revolving and repeating cannon.

94 Mortar-like cannon, a type
that was actually widely used.

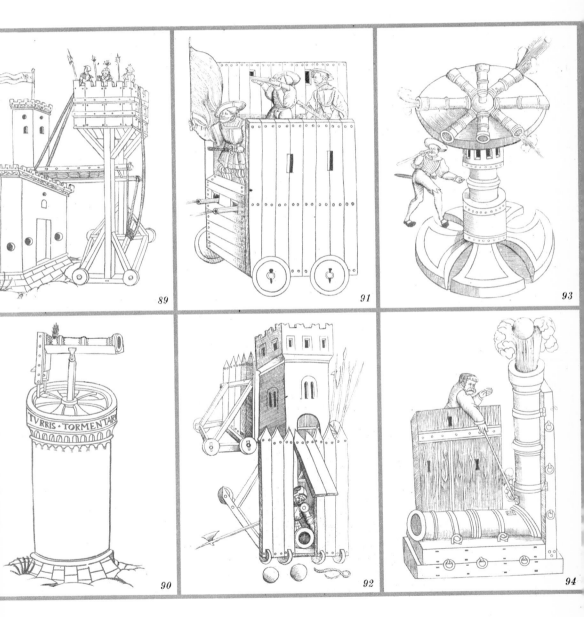

95 *A siege engine*
to end all siege engines,
this monster, shown in a copper
plate of 1588, was designed
to throw both incendiary shells
as well as heavy stones
into a beleagured town or fort.
Siege artillery, or cannon,
had been used with effect
since the fourteenth century—
for instance by the Turks
at the siege of Constantinople
in 1453. By the sixteenth century
artillery had been much improved,
yet more primitive machines
like this were still being designed.
In the same manner
suits of armor became heavier
and more complicated for a time
after the introduction of firearms.

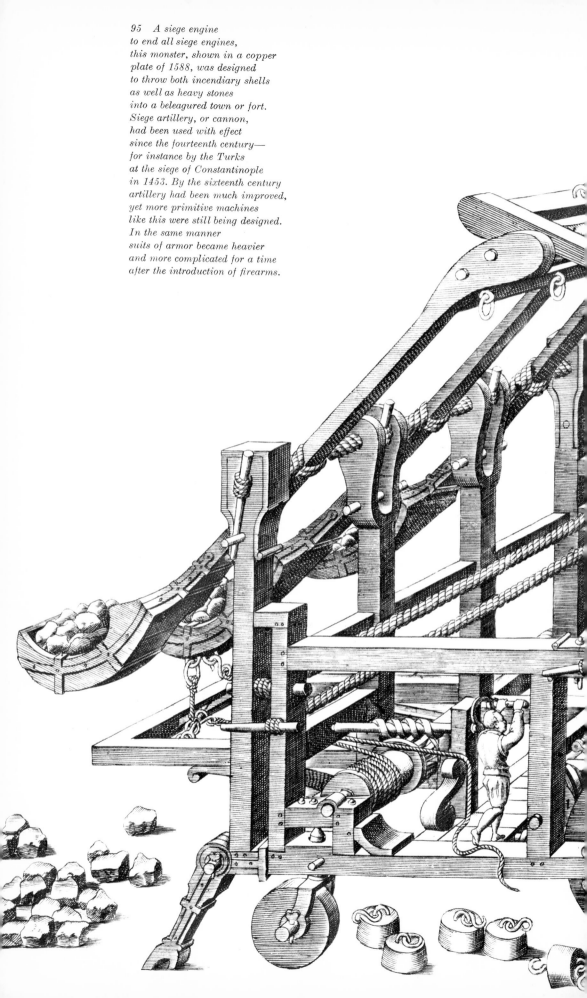

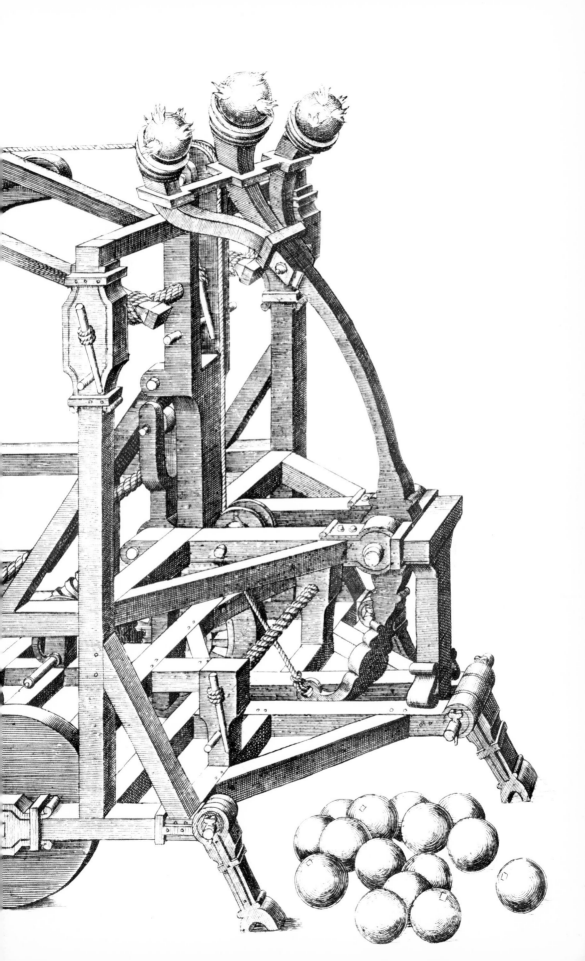

"glided forward in perfect order and in deep silence until the war cry burst out in one simultaneous roar and the column dashed itself against the solid front." The halberdiers, armed with a murderous eight-foot weapon combining an axe, a hook, and a point, were held for the final slashing attack. It was a Swiss halberd that struck down Leopold of Austria in 1386 and in 1477 laid open the head of Charles of Burgundy from crown to chin.

Yet the Middle Ages lingered on, for the knight and all he represented, having survived pike and bow, met the more serious threat of firearms with even more stubborn resistance. When firearms began to count in the fifteenth century he abandoned chain mail for full plate armor. And this, from the great bascinet or helm to the steel sabatons protecting the feet, often weighed as much as 300 to 400 pounds and required a special breed of heavy Flanders horse to carry the ensemble. The best armor was made in Italy and in Germany and was exported all over Europe. In the early sixteenth century the armorers went on to even greater refinements, such as the beautiful, incised "Maximilian" armor which succeeded the German "Gothic" of the previous century. But after this, armor rapidly declined, for the knight could not hold out indefinitely.

His stronghold or castle succumbed even earlier, leaving him ever more defenceless against the king or central power, who had artillery and professional troops at his command. Through the Middle Ages the castle, with its towers, curtain walls, machicolations, and inner and outer keeps had become ever stronger—and more numerous. It was a hard nut to crack; nevertheless, medieval warfare was largely taken up with protracted and elaborate sieges. First came the investment, almost amounting to the building of a castle around a castle, then the attempts to mine the walls, the bombardment with ballista and huge rock-throwing mangonels, the use of battering rams and of movable towers to surmount the ramparts, and finally the subjection from keep to keep and tower to tower. Or, more often the discouraged withdrawal.

With artillery, all of this changed. At the end of the Hundred Years' War French artillery had become the best in the world. In one year (1449-50) Charles VII was able to subdue 60 English strongholds in Normandy which formerly might have taken as much as a year each to reduce. Somewhat earlier Joan of Arc that symbol of the Middle Ages, had raised the English siege of Orleans with the help of artillery. In the first half of the century the Hussite rebels in Bohemia, under the gifted Jan Zizka defeated one medieval army after the other by means of cannon and hand gunners based on mobile forts of linked wagons (the old nomad *laager*). These were but curtain raisers for the Turkish siege of Constantinople in 1453, which featured the first organized bombardment in history—by 13 great bombards throwing stone shot weighing hundreds of pounds (they took two hours to load), and 56 smaller pieces.

Hard pressed by pike, bow, gun and cannon, the knight retreated more and more into a make-believe world of high chivalry and knightly sports—much as the Japanese knightly code, or Bushido, had reached its most

nystical form when the institution it represented was on the decline. Chivalry and Bushido
both began as warrior's codes, and in their
purest form emphasized loyalty and honor,
exalted the symbol of the sword, perpetuated
themselves by elaborate training and indoctri-
nation of the young initiate, and contained a
religious element. Chivalry came to its first
flowering during the crusades and by the late
twelfth century had been elaborated into a
rather frivolous system of courtly love backed
up by fulsome romances glorifying knightly
bravery and virtues and the exalted place of
women. As the feudal system began to break
down in the fourteenth century chivalry was
revived in even more exaggerated form. Another aspect of the knightly life was the tourna-
ment, originally a rough and bloody war game,
which, like chivalry, soon became refined into
a colorful, formalized spectacle that took
place under the admiring eyes of the ladies in
lists decorated with heraldic emblems and
painted in gold and bright colors.

While the knight took to the lists, ordinary
battles more and more began to be fought by
professional soldiers—especially by the high-
priced Swiss mercenary pikemen ("point d'ar-
gent, point de Suisse" was a saying of the time),
but also by *Landsknechten* (mercenary German
pikemen formed on the Swiss model) and by
Italian *Condottieri*, or mercenary bands, who
chose to wage the endless little fifteenth century
wars between Italian city states in full armor
and mounted like knights. But they were
hardly knights. Their military philosophy was
that of Machiavelli: "Although in all other
affairs it is hateful to use fraud, in the operations of war it is praiseworthy and glorious."
Under the spur of new technologies, and particularly the increasing use of gunpowder, war
had lost all semblance of idealism and chivalry;
it was becoming a science, with professional
officers probing the experience of the ancients
for new lessons. The Spanish infantry of Gon-
salvo de Cordova, which proved its superiority
over pikemen in Italy, was armed, like the
Roman legions, with thrusting sword, buckler,
and light armor.

The Italian wars between 1494 and 1525,
which pitted the French against the Haps-
burgs and other enemies, were military testing
grounds in which the old and new were inex-
tricably intermixed. Ravenna in 1512 saw the
first decisive use of artillery in the field. At
Marignano in 1515 the superb French artillery
of Francis I tore holes in the massed Swiss
phalanx of pikemen—but only to let in charge
after charge of medieval cavalry! Although the
pike did not disappear for many years, the
deep Swiss formation suffered in these wars
both from artillery and from the Spanish
infantry, ending the legend of Swiss invincibility. The artillery, moreover, subdued so
many ancient fortresses that a new type of
fortification, effective against the new cannon,
began to appear—wet ditches, and low-lying
earthworks and ramparts surmounted by
opposing guns. And finally an improved arquebus played havoc again with the hapless
Swiss under the direction of the Spanish
Marquis of Pescara. In many ways the Italian
wars, like the Italian Renaissance, marked
the end of the Middle Ages and the beginning
of a new era.

97-98   *Two positions from Pistofilo's
"Ceremony of the Tournement," early
seventeenth century. The medieval tournement,
which had started as a mock-war,
ended in this formal posturing.*

99 *Past and future
met at the Battle of Marignano
in 1515, when young Francis I
of France decisively defeated
the Swiss forces fighting
for the Emperor and Pope.
Massed French artillery tore holes
in the close ranks of Swiss pikemen,
clearing the way for the charge
of mounted knights,
as in medieval battle.
Yet the hardy Swiss,
whose phalanx of pikemen
and halberdiers had been the terror
of Europe for centuries, gave way
only after 30 cavalry charges,
and 28 hours of fighting.
German pikemen,
or "landsknechte," also fought
on the French side.*

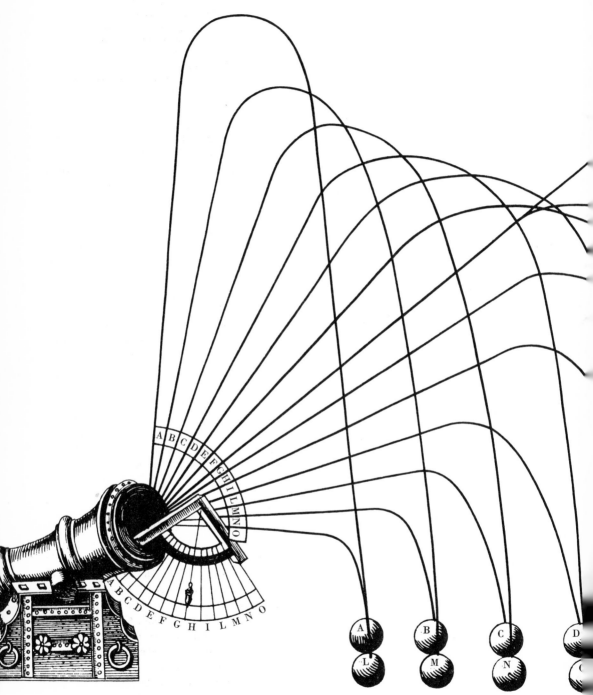

*100   How to use the quadrant
in calculating the trajectory of a cannon
ball—from a seventeenth century manual.
Firearms, introduced in the 1300's,
had become the dominant weapon
by the seventeenth century.*

The Italian wars were indeed the beginning of a new era. Henceforth, until the appearance of modern rocket missiles, the history of weapons would be the history of firearms. And firearms were something new in the world, presenting a possibility of organized destruction on a scale hitherto difficult to achieve. Western man wasted no time in using the new weapons to their full potential. The sixteenth century Religious Wars in France were bloody and cruel; the Thirty Years' War in the next century was, it has been said, "the most horrible single military episode in Western history." Thereafter, for a time, there was a revulsion which led to limited warfare; but with the French Revolution and Napoleon the bloodbath began all over again. Yet western man, from a very early date, also realized and deplored the new power of the gun. "O! curs'd device! base implement of death!" Ariosto fulminated. In the sixteenth century Blaise de Monluc, Marshal of France, called the arquebus "the Devil's invention to make us murther one another."

The origin of firearms, like that of most useful inventions, is obscure. The Chinese seem to have had gunpowder (whose basic ingredients are saltpeter, charcoal, and sulphur) by the eleventh century. By the thirteenth the industrious Arabs had passed it on to the West —and possibly the first primitive cannon as well. Certainly Roger Bacon, the scholar, had written about gunpowder before 1249, and there are well-authenticated accounts of cannon early in the next century. The first cannon were "firepots," crude iron buckets loaded with powder and stones and touched off through a

101 (Preceding page).
Manual of Arms,
early seventeenth century.
"Present the pike."
102-104 Musketeer
preparing to fire.
Bandolier holds wooden
tubes, each containing
powder and ball for
one shot. Forked stick
supports weight of barrel.
105-108 Helmeted
arquebusier loading
his weapon. Both ends
of match are kept alight.
109 (Opposite)
Cannoneer aims his weapon
for 1,000-yard shot.
From instruction book
by Ufano, 1621.

109

hole at the bottom. These simple siege engines soon gave way to the familiar tubular form, at first with barrels of brass or copper, later of iron. In the year of Crécy, 1346, cannon were used at the siege of Calais: "Thanked be God and Mary mild. / They hurt neyther man, woman, nor child." In the same century hand cannon weighing about ten pounds began to appear. The larger cannon, or bombards, were either fixed in place or dragged on sledges.

Indeed by the end of the fifteenth century almost every type of firearm in existence today was envisaged or invented—at least in crude form—including the brief appearance of a breechloader! Aside from artillery, whose early exploits have been touched upon, the most important invention was the matchlock arquebus, a most durable weapon which appeared early in the century and became the principal infantry firearm for the next 250 years. Introduced into Japan and the East in the 1600's, it survived in certain remote areas into modern times. The arquebus (from the German *Haken-büsche*, or hooked gun—the meaning of the "hook" is obscure), consisted of an iron barrel mounted on a stock which fitted against the chest. A cock holding a long burning fuse (slow match) was released by the trigger to bring it down on a pan holding the priming powder. The subsequent roar and cloud of sulphurous smoke as the main charge ignited convinced everybody that the gun was indeed the invention of Satan.

Although credulous soldiers squandered money on charms and talismans to ward off its effects, the arquebus was not a very accurate weapon. "In a skirmish," wrote a prejudiced observer, "there dieth not so many as one man for the Harquebusiers content themselves with making of a noyse, and so shoot at all adventure." Moreover the long, glowing match (as much as nine feet long), susceptible to rain or the eyes of enemy scouts, the weight of match that had to be carried along, the dampening or blowing away of the priming powder were all problems. Nevertheless the arquebus was an enormous improvement over the hand cannon.

In the long sporadic contest between Charles V and the Turks in the first half of the sixteenth century the superb Spanish infantrymen (these were the warriors who were conquering new empires in Mexico and South America) were armed in equal proportion with arquebus and pike, while the shock troops of the Turks, the Janissaries (slave children trained as a warrior caste) were equally masters of the arquebus. About mid-century the Spanish developed a new and heavier version of the arquebus, the musket, which was actually a small, matchlock hand-cannon with a one-inch bore. Because of its weight it had to be rested on an iron fork for firing, and took a full three minutes to load. The harassed musketeer of the day, festooned with an assortment of powder flasks, bullet pouches, and four-foot lengths of slow match, had to go through a complex series of motions before firing. Although the musket was soon reduced in size, it was used in a formation which varied little until the end of the eighteenth century, the first line of the square firing on command, then retiring to the rear to reload while the next line moved forward to fire. Separate units of armored pikemen protected the musketeers during the tedious process of

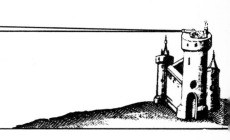

reloading—and the pike still delivered the major shock of the battle.

The wheellock, presumably developed from a design by Leonardo da Vinci, appeared in Nuremberg around 1520. It worked like a cigarette lighter, a spring-loaded wheel striking sparks from a flint into the priming pan. But the mechanism was too complex and expensive to make, and the wheellock shoulder gun never gained much acceptance as a military weapon. It was a favorite, however, with those who could afford it for themselves, and the more expensive arms were artistic creations, beautifully decorated with fine engravings or rare inlays. Charles V, who was a great gun fancier, once paid a fortune for a pair of Viennese matched pistols, and went to great lengths to introduce the art of gunmaking from Germany into Spain. Too complex for a mass weapon, the wheellock proved however to have a future as a one-handed gun, invented about 1540 as the "Pistolet," and later called the pistol. "Fetch me my pistolett" an English ballad of the 1550's goes, "And charge me my gonne,/ That I may shott at yonder bloddy butcher,/ The Lord of Easter-towne." Towards the end of the century the pistol, a foot long, was standard equipment for European cavalry, two in the holsters and one in the right boot.

Cavalry in fact, unable to stand up to arquebus and musket, had played a diminishing role until the pistol appeared. In the French Religious Wars after 1562 cavalry came back into its own, the Huguenots using it in long columns, armed with pistol and sword, for shock and raiding, while the more professional Catholic horsemen practised the difficult "caracole,"

line after line firing their pistols, then wheeling to the rear to reload. These wars, a series of bitter and exhausting massacres, persecutions, and civil wars until the Edict of Nantes brought peace in 1598, pitted Protestant merchants and tradesmen against the professional soldiers of the Catholics. The Huguenots, lacking artillery, and pikesmen to protect their hand-gunners while reloading (a most important consideration in those days!), resorted to flexible and ingenious tactics, developing the art of improvising fortifications, using the heavy musket at close range almost like artillery, and placing expendable arquebusiers, called "enfants perdus," in the wings and amongst the cavalry to break up the opposing cavalry formations.

It was much the same story during the Protestant revolt in the Netherlands against Spanish rule (1568-1609), the wily Dutch cutting the dikes to flood out the enemy, making sneak attacks on skates down frozen canals, and fortifying their towns so effectively that some held out for years. Their leader, young Maurice of Nassau, son of William the Silent, formed the untrained Dutch into the first dependable standing army, requiring long enlistment and strict discipline, but paying his troops regularly. Companies were small and supple, with pike and musket in equal proportion, the pikemen keeping three feet apart.

The manifold changes stemming from the introduction of firearms reached a first culmination in the devastating Thirty Years' War (1618-1648), which began as a religious revolt in Bohemia and finally involved most of Europe in a series of political struggles. The typical soldier was a low-grade, ruffianly mercenary,

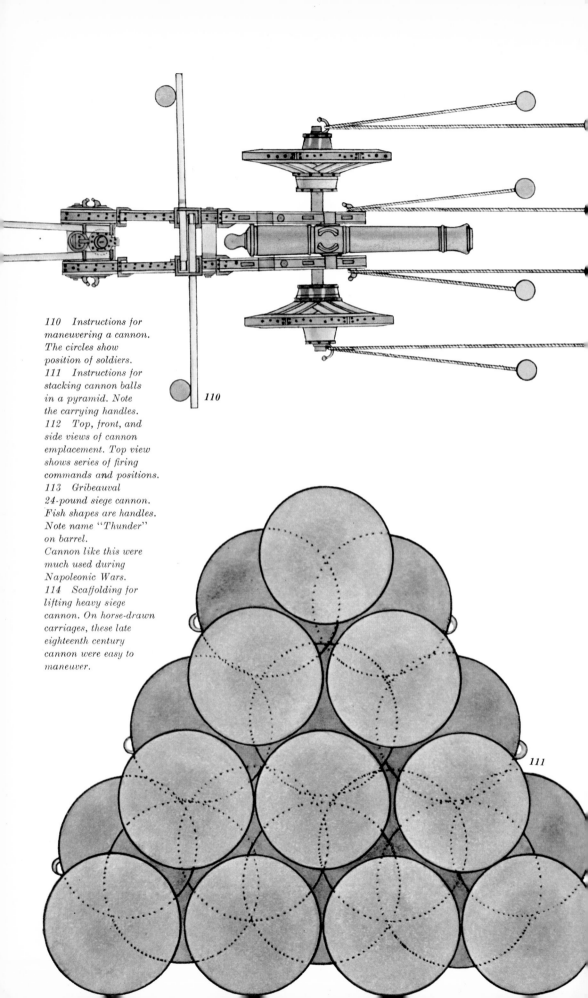

110   Instructions for
maneuvering a cannon.
The circles show
position of soldiers.
111   Instructions for
stacking cannon balls
in a pyramid. Note
the carrying handles.
112   Top, front, and
side views of cannon
emplacement. Top view
shows series of firing
commands and positions.
113   Gribeauval
24-pound siege cannon.
Fish shapes are handles.
Note name "Thunder"
on barrel.
Cannon like this were
much used during
Napoleonic Wars.
114   Scaffolding for
lifting heavy siege
cannon. On horse-drawn
carriages, these late
eighteenth century
cannon were easy to
maneuver.

110

111

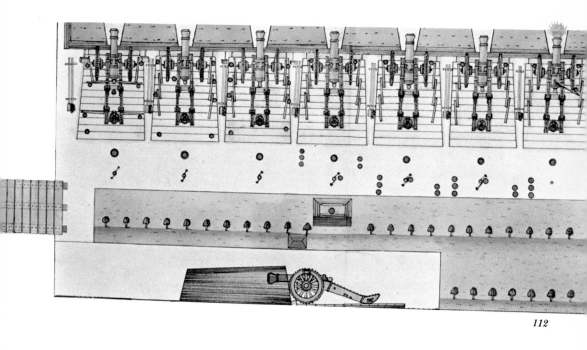

112

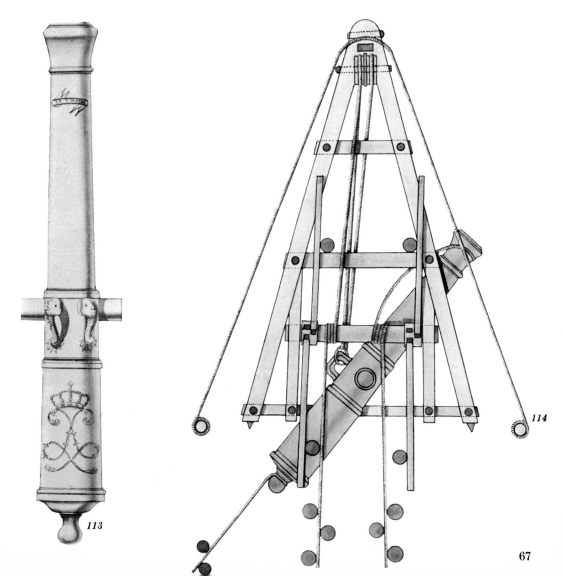

113

114

irregularly paid and employed, lacking morals or discipline, who lived off the land and terrorized the civilian population. Famine, pestilence, murder, and even cannibalism were so common that it has been said that between a third and a half of the German-speaking peoples of the time perished in these despicable wars.

An exception to the rule was the army of Gustavus Adolphus of Sweden in the 1630's. The first truly national army, it had its own uniform of blue and yellow and its own supply system. The army was well-disciplined, and promotion was strictly by merit. A brilliant general, Gustavus skillfully coordinated arms and artillery (pikesmen, musketeers, cavalry, and cannon), especially in the decisive battle of Breitenfeld. This was perhaps his greatest contribution, but he was also responsible for many innovations, some stemming from the earlier Religious Wars—prepared (paper-wrapped, cartridges for his musketeers, prepared ammunition (in wooden cases) for his cannon, the first lightly armored horse dragoons (attacking with pistols but dismounting to fight with swords), an engineering system copied from the Dutch, and a shortened pike. He sought to lighten cannon, developing, then discarding, a leather-covered field piece weighing only 90 pounds, then equipping each regiment with a light, wheeled four-pounder delivering grape and canister.

The English Civil Wars (1642-1649) could not be compared to the continental wars in ferocity or in techniques. Protected by her fleet, England had not developed the art of warfare, and armies on both sides were untrained and undisciplined. Innovations in arms were the screw barrel gun (the barrel screwing off to introduce the powder and ball), the introduction of the flintlock, and, probably as a result of the wars, the gradual rise of England to a pre-eminent position in gunmaking by 1750. The flintlock, which first appeared about 1630, was destined to become the favored firing mechanism until the middle of the nineteenth century. It had the enormous advantage of a cover over the pan which kept the priming powder dry in all weathers. The falling flint pushed the cover back while striking sparks to ignite the priming charge. Curiously enough a more primitive flintlock, the snaphaunce, invented over a century earlier, saw little military service. The rather similar miquelet, with a half-cock safety, was used by the Spanish with effect, but for various reasons the developed flintlock did not supplant the matchlock in continental armies until the 1680's. In England the flintlock musket "Brown Bess" was officially adopted in 1690.

After the close of the English wars in 1660 Europe, in profound revulsion against the turmoil and bloodshed of the previous era, entered upon a period of limited warfare which was a military counterpart to the famed "moderation" of the eighteenth century. "At the present day" wrote Emeric de Vattel "war is carried on by regular armies; the people, the peasantry, the townsfolk take no part in it, and as a rule have nothing to fear from the sword of the enemy." Under the Marquis de Louvois, Louis XIV's Minister of War, the line formation was introduced, a highly specialized tactical system devised for the open-field terrain of Europe. Trained by the famous Jean Martinet,

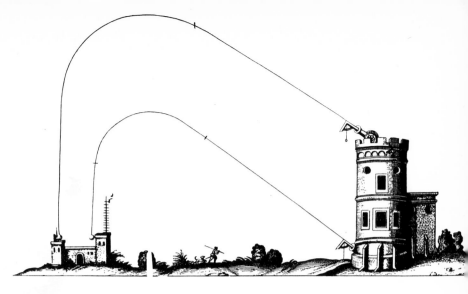

whose name has become a byword, the troops advanced in lines three deep, at 80 steps a minute, all guns at a precise angle, then fired volleys on command. A single "perfect volley," like that of Wolfe's at Quebec, could decide a general action. The pike had disappeared, for the combination of the socket bayonet, introduced around 1700, with the flintlock provided an all-purpose weapon. The modern infantry soldier had appeared.

The economy and science of warfare was evident, too, in the work of the great French military engineer, Sebastien le Prestre, Lord of Vauban, who built 33 forts and worked out an almost infallible system of besieging a city by means of a network of parallel and zigzag trenches. Louis XIV and his court used to take picnics to a nearby hill to watch—and lay bets on—the latest Vauban operation against an enemy city.

Another master of the science of warfare was Frederick the Great of Prussia whose troops (recruited, not mercenary) were so strictly disciplined that it is said they feared their officers more than the enemy. Frederick's introduction of horsedrawn artillery was one of the greatest tactical innovations of the period. His use of siege howitzers in the field was very effective. The battle of Fontenoy in 1745 brought in on Frederick's side one of the ablest soldiers and military writers of the period, Maurice de Saxe of France. Typical too of the times was the extreme formality (as well as the popularity) of duels, fought usually with matched flintlock duelling pistols—slender, reliable weapons with nine- or ten-inch octagonal barrels.

During the American Revolution some of the ideological fervor and unorthodox methods of the later Napoleonic period began to creep back into warfare. At Valley Forge, it is true, Prussian Baron von Steuben beat European discipline into the American army, while the usual smoothbore musket was the principal arm on both sides. A regiment of 500 British redcoats, armed with the durable "Brown Bess," could loose a volley of 250 shots every fifteen seconds—and often did to the dismay of the Americans. On the other hand, the redcoats sometimes found themselves in situations where the disciplined "hail of fire" technique counted for little, especially when they faced American frontiersmen in broken terrain, firing their deadly rifles from behind every tree or hillock in the Indian manner. Daniel Morgan's riflemen, for instance, were described as a "fierce, illiterate, cougar-like lot ... clad in filth-encrusted buckskin moccasins, leggins, breeches, hunting shirts and fur caps." But they stopped the British at Freeman's Farm in 1777. Their famous "Kentucky" or long rifle (the spin imparted to the bullet by the grooved barrel making it accurate at 150 yards) had been developed from the much heavier European rifle, long used for hunting and target practice and brought to America by German immigrants. Light and graceful, it had a slim stock, small bore (40-45 caliber), and a slender, five-foot barrel. Despite the success of this weapon, the rifle, too expensive and difficult to handle, was avoided by the military for many years.

The French Revolution brought on profound changes in warfare, though very little in weapons. Against the sluggish armies of the

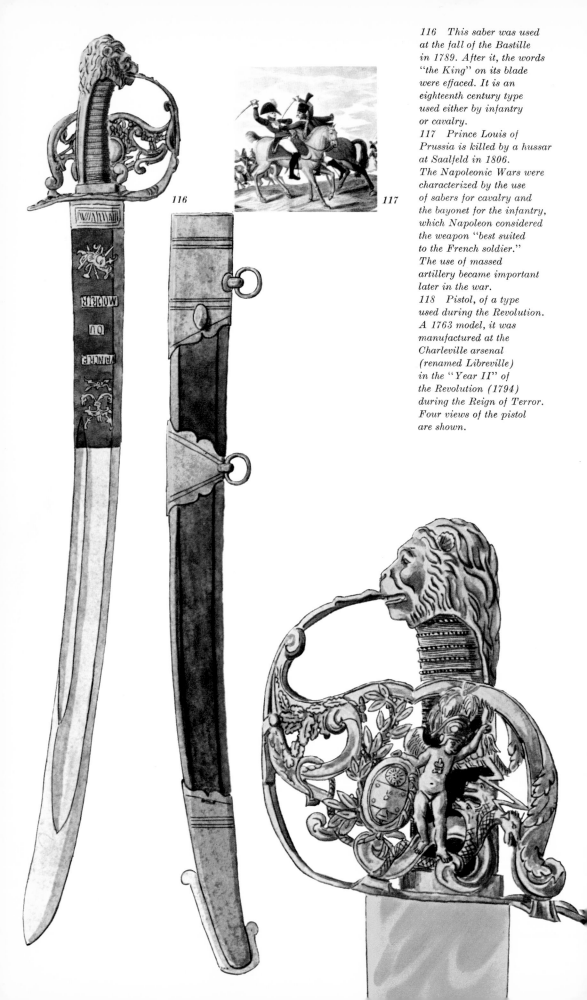

116   This saber was used at the fall of the Bastille in 1789. After it, the words "the King" on its blade were effaced. It is an eighteenth century type used either by infantry or cavalry.

117   Prince Louis of Prussia is killed by a hussar at Saalfeld in 1806. The Napoleonic Wars were characterized by the use of sabers for cavalry and the bayonet for the infantry, which Napoleon considered the weapon "best suited to the French soldier." The use of massed artillery became important later in the war.

118   Pistol, of a type used during the Revolution. A 1763 model, it was manufactured at the Charleville arsenal (renamed Libreville) in the "Year II" of the Revolution (1794) during the Reign of Terror. Four views of the pistol are shown.

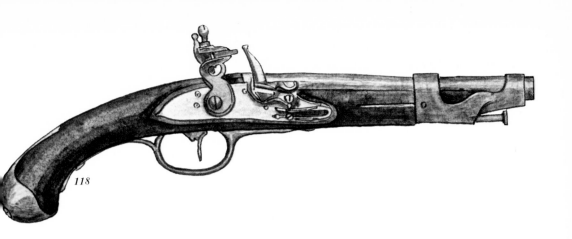

118

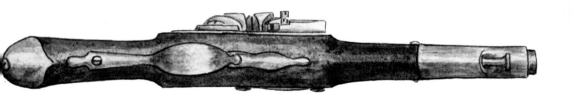

First Coalition the National Conscription Act of 1793 brought out a peoples' army, determined "to advance until complete destruction." Mass attack, in long shouting columns of bayonet-wielding citizens, was substituted for the line formation, and an undisciplined firing at will for the volley at command. Such tactics took the enemy by surprise, and victory for a time was easy. But as the revolutionary élan ebbed, new tactics, based upon the immensely popular writings of the Comte de Guibert, were devised to fit the new type of army— first by General Lazare Carnot of the revolutionary armies, and then by Napoleon. The troops lived off the land, increasing their mobility. Thanks to conscription, the armies were larger (Napoleon led nearly a half-million men into Russia in 1812), and could thus be broken into divisional and smaller units, with subordinate commanders (Napoleon started as one himself). Divisions could separate for movement, then concentrate for attack, or the enemy's plans could be frustrated by engaging him at several points at once, or in the rear. These tactics brought the commander-in-chief into a new prominence. Napoleon himself relied upon instant intuition to shape a battle while in progress, often extending his front to outflank the enemy.

The infantry was king in these conscript armies of the period, the cavalry under Napoleon usually playing a subordinate role as a scouting force or a tactical force for pursuit. In his earlier campaigns Napoleon put great trust in the bayonet, calling it "the arm best suited to the French soldier." But as the quality of his infantry declined (by 1812 at least two thirds of his armies were foreign, and largely untrained) he turned to the massed use of artillery in all phases of battle. "It is with artillery that war is made," he said, following the doctrines of the Chevalier de Theil in the previous century. But the artillery itself he had in abundance, thanks to General Gribeauval, who, beginning in 1765, had completely reorganized the French artillery, dividing it into field, garrison, and siege guns. He introduced the concept of uniform models and interchangeable parts (although unlike Eli Whitney in America in 1780, he did not go into the manufacturing of these parts), and the use of wheeled limber boxes for carrying ammunition and to provide a seat for the gunners. Napoleon used massed batteries of Gribeauval's light 12-pounder field piece with effect at the pivotal battle of Friedland in 1807 and subsequently at Wagram (1809) and Borodino (1812).

Relying on mass attack, Napoleon employed few of the new weapons which were beginning to appear at the end of the wars. The British, on the contrary, used howitzers; the shrapnel shell, a murderous projectile invented by Henry Shrapnel in 1784; and even a force of riflemen, the famous Light Division. But Napoleon was primarily defeated by his own limitations. Depending upon surprise and aggressive tactics, he was at a loss when on the defensive. Moreover, the size of his armies and his growing tendency to keep his plans to himself created a dangerous absence of communication. At Waterloo his orders were not understood, and at the crucial moment one division failed to appear. Intuition could go just so far and no further.

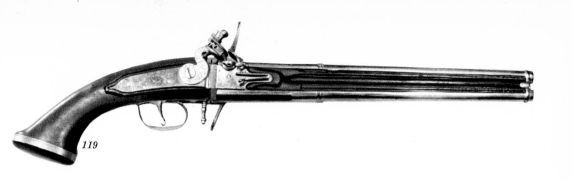

119

120

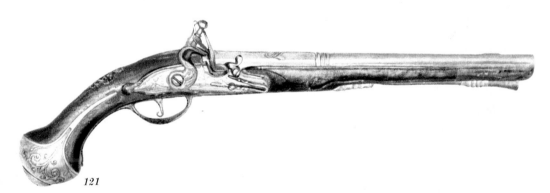

121

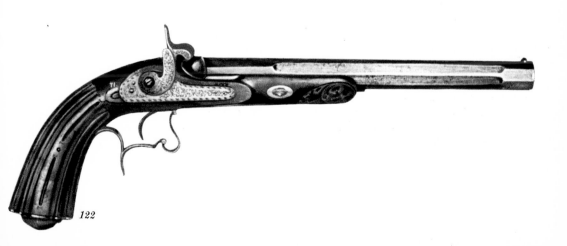

122

123   *Desperate last resistance of the Paris Commune
in 1871. Old muzzle-loading cannon was seized
from regular troops. More typical of the period
was rifled and breech-loading artillery,
invented in 1859 and dominant up through World War I.*

During the period between the appearance of the first crude cannon and the end of the eighteenth century the world had seen uncounted varieties of firearms, of all sizes and shapes —matchlock, wheellock, and flintlock; single shooters and repeaters; the tiny, handsomely decorated pistol for a lady's purse and the massive siege gun. But all (with the exception of a variety of purely experimental models) worked on a common principle: the powder and projectile were rammed down the barrel, then discharged by a burning match or the flash of priming powder. By contrast, the nineteenth century saw the greatest advance in firearms development in history. There was an impressive growth in the size and power of artillery. The traditional muzzle-loading bronze cannon of the eighteenth century, with its slim lines, gave way by mid-century to heavy, reinforced steel monsters—like the fixed siege cannon of Krupp—breechloading and rifled, firing a conical projectile that could weigh as much as 1,000 pounds. More powerful propellants, such as various early forms of smokeless powders, appeared, while the charge within the shell was also strengthened and fuses were made more reliable. Toward the end of the century the recoil shock was checked by hydraulic or hydropneumatic buffers, greatly increasing the rate of fire.

The progress in small arms mechanisms, though less spectacular, was more revolutionary. In 1807 Dr. Alexander Forsyth, a minister with a passion for guns, patented a device which has been called the greatest advance in firearms since the invention of gunpowder. Instead of the clumsy flint and priming powder system, the hammer struck a bit of detonating compound in the touch hole, such as mercury fulminate, which set off the main charge by exploding rather than burning. This simple device laid the basis for the development of breechloaders and self-contained cartridges—but its adoption was slow. "I cannot deny that Mr. Forsyth's invention offers many vulgar advantages," wrote a British gentleman in 1817. "True sportsmen, however, do not require the new lock, for a good flint-lock will answer every conceivable purpose a gentleman might wish."

Joe Manton, the greatest gunsmith in England, developed a metallic tube to hold a single charge of fulminate, and possibly also the copper percussion cap, which contained a bit of primer and fitted onto a nipple at the breech. It had appeared on both sides of the Atlantic by 1820. In the 1830's the new system was finally adopted by the military, and in 1835 went into the first successful revolver, invented by the American, Samuel Colt. Earlier revolvers had often blown up when all chambers fired at once, but Colt avoided this by recessing his percussion nipples. And he manufactured his revolvers on the interchangeable parts system, thus reducing their price to an attractive level.

The rifle was becoming increasingly popular, but the problem of forcing a bullet down the barrel against the resistance of the rifling remained. The American frontiersmen had used a greased patch to facilitate loading, but still too much gas pressure escaped on firing. In 1847 Captain Charles Minié of the French army devised his famous "minnie ball," a paper-wrapped cartridge with a hollow-based bullet which slipped easily down the barrel. The base expanded on firing to fit snugly into the rifle grooves, ensuring an effective gas seal. This was a great advance, but the next step was to do away with muzzle-loading altogether. The most important of the early breechloading rifles was the Dreyse needle gun, invented in 1838, adopted by the Prussian army in 1842.

The final invention that produced the basic modern rifle—and effectively solved the problem of gas-sealing—was the metallic, self-contained cartridge, providing bullet, propellant, and primer in one unit. Its copper case expanded on firing to seal the breech, then immediately contracted to allow for easy extraction (automatic ejection of the case did not come until later). French gunmaker Lefaucheux's pin-fire cartridge, very popular in Europe, came in 1836. The rim-fire cartridge, developed by Flobert in France about the same time, was improved by Smith and Wesson in the United States for their .22 caliber revolver of 1857, first to use a cartridge. The center-fire system, suitable for high-powered cartridges, was invented in 1860 and has changed little to this day.

Startling as were these advances in weaponry, the military adopted them very slowly, for the average officer of the period either resisted all innovation completely or held that it was impossible to advance beyond Napoleon. The Crimean War of 1854 to 1856, between France, Turkey, and England on one side and Russia on the other, was obscure in its motivation and a confusion of misdirection and bungling in its execution. Tennyson has aptly described one

124 Wilhelm Bauer's system
for fording rivers. A mortar shell,
to which a cable is attached,
is fired from one shore to the other.
System dates from 1854.
125 Bauer gun carriage and limber.
Driver sat on top of limber box.
Coil spring absorbed weight of heavy
cannon over rough ground.
126 Revolving gun battery was set
in a deep pool of water,
could easily be swung to face attack
coming from land or sea. This is another
of Bauer's inventions and dates from 1862
Note that cannon are all
muzzle-loaders.
Most progress was in the field of mounts,
carriages, and recoil-reducing mechanisms
Not all of Bauer's designs were
to see active use.

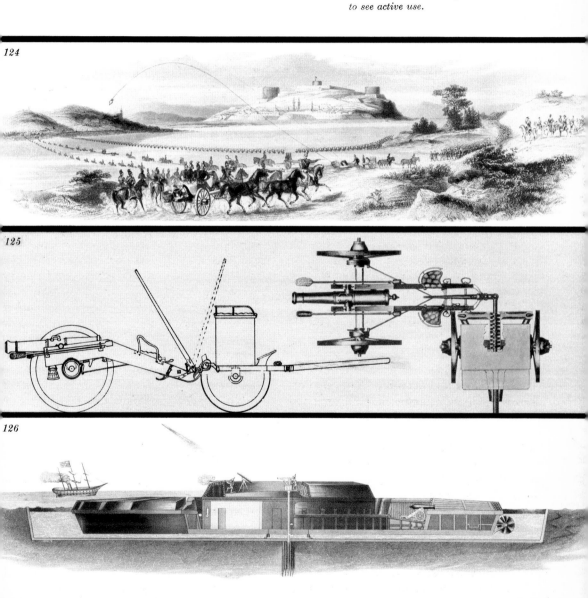

124

125

126

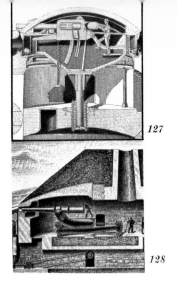

127

128

typical incident in "The Charge of the Light Brigade." Although breechloaders were already in service, none appeared at the front; instead the Russians were armed with the smoothbore and the Allies with an assortment of flintlocks, muskets, percussionlocks, and rifles. The Minié ball was used, but in its original large caliber was not very effective. Despite the efforts of Florence Nightingale, most casualties came from epidemic and infection. The brief war between Austria and France three years later was not much more inspiring, though Napoleon III did employ the first breechloading, rifled cannon. Aside from this, as Philip Guedalla has written, the French enjoyed the "pleasing experience of defeating with the methods of 1809 an adversary whose military thought was that of 1759."

The American Civil War started in 1861 in much the same way, for in its isolation the United States had developed little military tradition and its standing army was pitifully small. Significantly, every officer, North or South, knew Baron Jomini's 1836 analysis of the Napoleonic experience by heart but had scarcely heard of von Clausewitz's "Vom Kriege" of 1832, which advocated a total "bloody solution" in warfare and the superiority of numbers over skill. But the Civil War soon became a Clausewitz war. It was marked by the mass production of weapons and supplies; the first extensive use of railroads in warfare; the employment of the military telegraph to good effect; the first battle between ironclad ships; the first appearance of a railway gun; the first naval ship sunk by a submarine; the use of military observation balloons, land

mines, and grenades; and above all by the modern idea of the systematic destruction of enemy resources and demoralization of the civilian population.

For the first time, too, the soldier was subordinated to his firepower. At the bloody battle of Shiloh in 1862 it is estimated that 80 per cent of the troops had never been in combat. Rifled guns which could kill up to 500 yards, even in the hands of greenhorns, soon doomed the cavalry charge, and eventually drove both sides into trenches. It is said that General Robert E. Lee's greatest innovation in weapons was the spade, for the South, hard put to match the firepower of the North, showed great ingenuity in defensive warfare, including the use of artillery, and riflemen dug into defensive "foxholes." And the South, like the soldiers of revolutionary France, lived off the land. "The path to glory," one of their generals remarked, "cannot be followed with much baggage."

Despite the new weapons available, the conservative North purchased and issued enormous quantities (over four million) of muzzle-loading rifles designed for the Minié ball. Nudged by Lincoln, the Ordnance Department finally began to issue a few breechloaders and repeaters, and by the end of the war had officially adopted some 120 different models of rifles, muskets, and pistols, (including the popular 1860 Army Model .44 caliber Colt revolver). Among repeating rifles the seven-shot Spencer of 1860 was preferred, for its cheapness and simplicity, over the 12-shot Henry (called by the Southerners "that damned Yankee rifle that can be loaded on Sunday and fired

127   Late nineteenth
century breech-loading
cannon under protective
dome. A forerunner of the
Maginot Line type of fort.
128   Mounted on recoil-
absorbing slide, 138 mm
cannon fires
from fortification.
129   English sailors firing
early machine gun very
similar to crank-operated
Gatling Gun of 1862.
130   Krupp cannon,
sensation of Paris
Exposition of 1867.

129

130

all week"). Over 60,000 Spencers were issued
to about 2,000 of the Henry. The breechloading, single-shot Sharps rifle of 1848 (its
accuracy fathered our word "sharpshooter")
was extremely popular, over 80,000 having
been issued. It became famous as a buffalo gun
after the war.

Artillery was used throughout the war in
large quantities. Napoleonic six- and 12-pound
bronze smoothbores were effective for hurling
grape and canister, but were inadequate against
the range of rifled muskets. Rifled, breechloading artillery—the Model 1861 3-inch cast
iron rifle, the Parrott gun, and the Brooke
gun—were introduced early in the war, and
while they had the range they did not have the
power of the older smoothbores. So both were
used, often in massive concentrations in
Napoleonic style. Enormous mortars, some of
the largest mounted on shipboard, were also
a feature of the war.

To Europe, lost in a Napoleonic dream, the
American Civil War was a war of "armed mobs
chasing each other around the country, from
which nothing could be learned." But Prussian
troops, led by Count von Moltke, a pupil of
Clausewitz, soon demonstrated that a modern
war could be fought in Europe too. In a lightning attack on Austria in the summer of 1866
Bismarck not only gained hegemony in Germany but revealed the strength of his well-
planned fighting machine. Bismarck then
turned on France in 1870 and though the
French fought valiantly, seeking to maintain
the Napoleonic offensive, they were cut to
pieces by the superior massed artillery of the
Prussians (most of the steel field pieces were

supplied by the young Essen firm of Krupp).
Having actively prepared for war, the Prussians exhibited a masterly coordination of
forces and plans, a strategic use of the railroads like that of the Civil War, and a flexible
command system that allowed subordinates
much freedom of decision (whereas the French
clung to the Napoleonic central command,
but had no good central commander).

The French, however, had several advantages.
Since the Prussians were armed with the Dreyse
needle gun, the French developed the breechloading Chassepot rifle, which had a greater
rate of fire than the Dreyse. Rejecting the
American Gatling gun, they adopted their own
Montigny machine gun, a weapon which, with
around 30 barrels and carriage, weighed over
two tons. It was introduced in great secrecy.
The Prussians first met it at the battles of
Gravelotte and Saint-Privat. Unfortunately
it was used at great range, almost like artillery
instead of tactically, and was easily destroyed
by the Prussian cannon. Dr. Richard Gatling's
original machine gun, invented in 1862, saw
little service during the Civil War, although it
could fire from 200 to 800 rounds per minute.
It had many predecessors, none of them
successful—including the Puckle Gun, patented
in England in 1718, which was supposed to
fire round bullets against Christians and
square bullets against infidels! In 1884 Hiram
Maxim invented the first automatic recoil-
operated machine gun. This water-cooled
weapon had a cyclic rate of fire of 600 rounds
per minute, and unlike the Gatling had
a single barrel and a belt feed rather than a
hopper. The rival Hotchkiss system used the

131 *General Ulysses S. Grant.*

gas created by the exploding cartridges to operate the action, a system extensively used in automatic rifles today.

In 1884, too, the first really successful smokeless powder, a gelatinized mixture of nitroglycerin and guncotton, appeared in France. Designed to avoid the revealing clouds of smoke released by the old blackpowder, it also proved to be far more stable and powerful and thus was responsible for a revolution in tactics; for greater range and penetration could now be given to ammunition which was lighter and smaller than before. In rifles, after much experimentation, the turnbolt action was developed to take high-powered cartridges (the popular Winchester repeater action, for instance, was too weak), notably in the Mauser Model 1898 with staggered, clip-loading flush magazine, the granddaddy of all bolt action rifles in use today. Revolvers at this time were being supplanted in military service by semi-automatic pistols like the Borchardt of 1893 which became the beautifully balanced and accurate Luger. This weapon, using a toggle (knee) system, was used by the German army between 1908 and 1938. Until 1911, when the Americans adopted the Browning .45, the U.S. Army had used the famous .45 Colt Single Action revolver. The Frontier Model (.44/40), used in the West, was often called the "Peacemaker" or "Equalizer."

The Russo-Japanese conflict (1904-1905) was the only real testing ground between 1871 and 1914 for the new weapons and theories. While naval clashes, using mines and torpedoes, were important, the land fighting featured the machine gun, the Japanese being armed with the Hotchkiss, the Russians with the Maxim. Though the latter proved more reliable, the Japanese used a small-bore rifle with light ammunition to good effect. The weight of fire, in this "modern" war indeed drove both sides into trenches very similar to those of World War I. Perhaps the most ominous lesson of the war, however, was the power that a modern military establishment could give a hitherto undeveloped nation like Japan.

But the first real test of modern armaments, if not of tactics, was World War I, which, with a few exceptions, was fought with the weapons described in this chapter. Each belligerent had a repeating rifle—the German Mauser, the British Lee-Enfield, the Austrian Mannlicher, the French Lebel, the American Springfield. Machine guns and semi-automatic pistols had already proved their worth. There was artillery in abundance, from the huge German 17-inch howitzer to the mobile French 75 mm. Though mostly in primitive form, the airplane, railroad, automobile, and wireless and radio communications were all available.

When the war opened the massive weight of fire brought to bear on the battlefield was not unexpected—but nobody could have anticipated its results. The French still dreamed of the Napoleonic offensive, the Germans of 1870, but in the end both ended up in the trenches for four bloody years. More machine guns were called for and even heavier artillery barrages; but these only made matters worse, pinning down the troops, churning up the forward territory so that advances became almost impossible. The Germans, incidentally, were well equipped with Maxim machine guns at the

133

134

138 139

140

143

144

133   *Siege cannon, 1870.*
134   *Late nineteenth century fort.*
135-137   *Maxim machine gun.*
138   *"Bange" 1870 cannon breech.*
139   *Colonel de Bange-reformer*
     of the French artillery,
     1870-1880.
140   *Krupp field piece, 1880.*
141   *Repeating rifles:*
     top, Mannlicher; middle,
     Winchester; bottom,
     Lee-Metford.
142   *French revolver of 1874, 11 mm.*
143   *"Bange" cannon, 220 mm.*
144   *Giant Krupp cannon,*
     which fired 1,000-pound
     shell (see 130).
145   *Alfred Krupp, 1812-1877.*
146   *Rapid-fire Maxim*
     field piece, 175 mm.

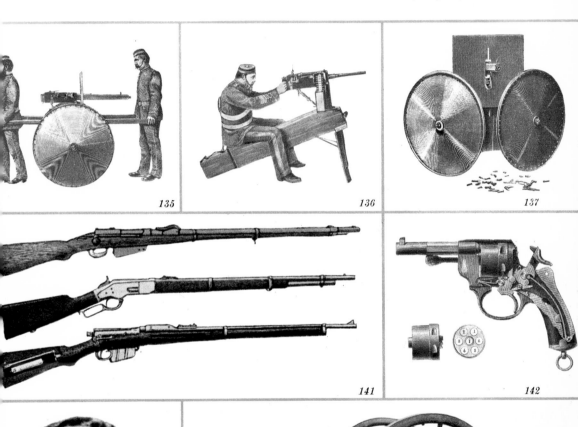

135   *136*   *137*

141   *142*

145

146

147　Heavy artillery barrages
and the extensive use of the machine gun
drove World War I armies
into trenches such as this one.

148 Not monsters, but gasmask-wearing civilians stare out of the window of a house which has just been hit by a bomb.

start of the war, but the French had very few machine guns, the British only two per battalion, and the Americans none (though they did have large numbers of Browning automatic rifles). France finally produced thousands of air-cooled Hotchkisses while England concentrated on the Vickers, and the United States on an American version of the same gun as well as the Browning machine gun.

The war had actually begun as a war of movement, the Germans sweeping down through Belgium, easily reducing, with their huge howitzers, the strong Belgian forts and reaching within 25 miles of Paris by August, 1914. But then, after General Galliéni had stemmed the German advance at the Battle of the Marne by rushing reinforcements forward in 600 taxicabs from Paris, the stalemate set in. By November both sides had settled into a complex line of trenches stretching from Switzerland to the North Sea (with a miniature set between Austria and Italy) which scarcely shifted more than ten miles for the rest of the war. Right up to the end both sides tried desperately to break out of the stalemate, to re-establish mobility, but it proved impossible. The early French bayonet attacks resulted in losses as high as 80 per cent. The Germans tried a breakthrough at Verdun in 1916 and failed. In 1918 their tactics of infiltration proved promising, but could not be followed up. Mobility was at the mercy of firepower.

Failing a breakthrough, other diversions, large and small, were tried. In 1915 the Allies attempted to turn the German flank at Gallipoli but ended up again in trenches and had to withdraw. The German shelling of Paris by "Big Bertha" in 1918 was not much more than a magnificent gesture. Somewhat more serious was the bombing of London, first by Zeppelins, then by Gotha bombers. Most serious of all was the submarine threat; but even this was overcome by 1918. In the meantime the dead piled up at the trenches. By 1917 both sides were exhausted, and near mutiny. The intervention of fresh troops from America may well have tipped the balance towards victory.

The means were actually at hand for breaking the stalemate, but all were still in primitive form: the tank, the airplane, fast wheeled transport, and a developed strategy of mobile, concentrated assault. These were to be features of the next world war. Fortunately poison gas, tried out locally by the Germans in 1915 and by the French the next year, did not recur. The tank was a British innovation. Lumbering Mark I, a 28-ton fortress armed with machine guns and cannon and capable of only four miles per hour, went into action in February, 1916, got mired in the mud, and was withdrawn. Tried again in 1917, the tank finally proved its usefulness—and the Germans never developed a defence against it. The airplane, quite primitive at the war's start, underwent an amazing transformation, evolving into bombers, fighters, and scouts, acquiring machine guns and even cannon, and participating in formation duels as well as massive assaults. By 1918 the larger factories were capable of producing up to 20,000 or 30,000 planes a year. And yet on the whole the airplane had very little to do with the outcome of the first world war.

149   Mobile German panzer unit in World War II.
After the over-static trench warfare of World War I
both sides took care to retain mobility at all costs.
Yet in other respects World War II
was a larger version of World War I.

Some 13 million soldiers and an equal number of civilians were killed in World War I and perhaps 20 million wounded. In revulsion against the firepower that had produced such slaughter, the victorious nations turned to disarmament and the League of Nations, while limiting their military establishments to a defensive role. Britain hoped to rely upon naval blockade for defence. France built her heavily fortified Maginot Line to discourage further German aggression. But certain professional soldiers, knowing that war would come again, drew different conclusions from the experience of World War I. Trench warfare must be avoided at all costs; mobility and the power of the offensive must be restored. In France and England Colonel Charles de Gaulle and General J.F.C. Fuller rejected passive defence, advocating the mechanized offensive, speed, and increased firepower. General "Billy" Mitchell of the United States and General Guilio Douhet of Italy preached the doctrine of strategic bombing, the latter predicting "the involvement of all people in the war of the future due to extensive aerial bombardment."

These men were indeed prophets, for although few new weapons were developed for World War II, the old weapons, particularly offensive ones, had been made far more effective. The airplane now flew at 300 miles per hour. The tank, armed with machine gun, cannon, or flame-thrower, could travel at 30 miles per hour. Artillery had become motorized and fast trucks provided the necessary transport. Mobility had been restored and the trench was a nightmare of the past.

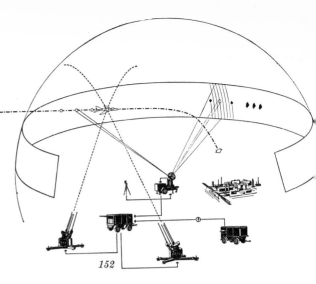

152

While England and the United States let their defences deteriorate and France built up an army on the World War I model, defeated Germany actually put the new concepts into practice. The "blitzkrieg" was first tried out in the Spanish war of 1936, proving that the strongest defensive line could be broken by a concentrated, mechanized tank assault preceded by intensive bombing and accompanied by dive-bombers. Once a breakthrough had been made the blitzkrieg fanned out laterally in a zigzag pattern, exploiting every weakness. The new tactic worked to perfection in the early years of World War II, partly because the enemy was ill-prepared and was taken by surprise. In 1939 Poland fell in 27 days. In 1940, after the Maginot Line had been by-passed, Holland fell in five days, Belgium in 18, and France in 39. Later victims were Yugoslavia, Greece, and Crete, the latter taken by a superbly staged aerial paratrooper assault. But in the depths of Russia, after the 1941 invasion, the edge of the blitzkrieg was blunted, especially by the giant 280, 305 and 406 mm Russian howitzers. In North Africa at the same time, antitank guns, land mines, and especially the American hand-rocket "bazooka" further took the measure of the German tank, giving the infantry new strength against it.

In the far Pacific the Japanese, exploiting the new tactics of the offensive in their own way, crippled the United States in 1941 with a concentrated surprise attack upon Pearl Harbor and the Phillipines by carrier-based planes, then moved out quickly to conquer an empire that stretched from the Aleutians to India. The Japanese soldiers, superbly trained, were masters of jungle warfare and guerilla fighting, specializing in camouflage and concealment, using mortars, snipers, and small tanks to good effect.

But the Allies, once they had recovered from the initial blows of the Germans and Japanese, developed an offensive strategy of their own. The Americans wore down the Japanese fleet with warships and carriers, and cut the sea lanes of Japan with a concentrated submarine attack. Above all they perfected the art of the massive amphibious landing assault—a land-sea parallel to the blitzkrieg. A coordinated combination of land, sea, and air operations, the amphibious technique had been studied by the United States Navy and Marine Corps since 1933, and in its developed form was one of the major tactical innovations of the war. It prepared the way for the invasion of countless Pacific islands as well as of Europe and Africa, and without a single major defeat. The most massive of all amphibious landings was the June 6, 1944 "D-Day" invasion of Normandy, which opened up occupied Europe to the Allies. Another Allied specialty, brought to fruition in the United States by the disciples of General Mitchell, was the strategic bombing of military, industrial, and civilian targets deep within enemy territory by tremendous fleets of four-engined bombers. The B-29 "fire raids" on Japan late in the war certainly contributed to her defeat. There is more argument about the effectiveness of the repeated large raids on Germany, Italy, and occupied Europe by Allied bombers.

Small arms basically changed very little between World War I and II. The bolt action rifles and many of the machine guns were the

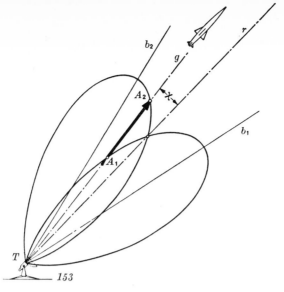

150 (Previous page,)
Fireball of atomic bomb
exploded over Nagasaki,
Japan, August 9, 1945.
Atom bomb, carried as
warhead by rocket missiles,
has proved to be most
potent weapon of our times.
151 (Previous page.)
U.S. Nike Ajax ground-to-
air missile, typical of a whole
arsenal of small rocket
weapons recently developed.
152 Electronic aiming
device used with
Hispano-Suiza
antiaircraft battery.
153 Radio guidance of
Swiss Oerlikon
ground-to-air rocket.

same. Most characteristic of World War II was the increase in automatic and semi-automatic weapons. At the beginning of the war only the United States had a semi-automatic rifle as infantry issue, the Garand, but soon both semi-automatic and fully automatic rifles were in general use, examples of the latter being the Russian Dektyarov and German FG 42. The British, with no semi-automatic rifle until after the war, relied heavily on the light, fully automatic, Sten submachine gun, which they also supplied to resistance forces in Europe. Among light machine guns the British Bren Gun was outstanding, as well as the widely used German MG 34, an all-purpose weapon designed to do the work of light, medium, and heavy machine guns. To answer the need for light, accurate selective fire weapons, the Americans developed the M-1 and M-2 carbines, the Germans the MP 43 and MP 44, both noted for their ease of handling.

Motorized and with rubber tires, artillery became mobile and more flexible. The Germans developed their 105 mm piece into a combination gun and howitzer for infantry use, and their famous "88" served as field gun, anti-tank, and antiaircraft gun in one. The development of recoilless artillery did away with the need for heavy mounts to absorb recoil and further increased the mobility of artillery. Another important advance was the American VT ("proximity") fuse, first used in the Battle of the Bulge, which detonated the shell within effective range of the target. Probably the most horrible weapons developed in World War II were the flame weapons—artillery shells filled with white phosphorus, airborne napalm bombs, or tank and portable flame-throwers.

Although World War II was largely fought with new versions of old weapons, there were hints of the warfare and the weapons of the future. The major belligerents employed batteries of small rocket weapons—the British Z-gun, the Russian "Katiusha," the German Nebelwerfer, the American 4.5 and 7.2-inch rockets—for saturation bombardment. There was the German V-2 ballistic missile with its frightening 200-mile range but small explosive impact; and finally, and above all, the first two atomic bombs dropped by the Americans on Japan in 1945, bringing death to some 150,000 people and suffering to many more. When the descendants of these first atomic bombs and of the V-2 were mated as warhead and delivery vehicle, the terror weapon of today became a reality. But long before this the United States, with its fleet of bombers capable of carrying the atom bomb to any point in the globe, felt so secure that it allowed its wartime military establishment to deteriorate. The illusion of security and the atomic monopoly lasted only a few years, for in 1949 the Soviets exploded their first bomb, and the next year the United States became involved in the Korean War.

Here was the turning point. From now on military strategy would be determined by the necessity, on the one hand, to fight limited wars with conventional arms, and on the other to keep constantly prepared for the unimaginable full-scale nuclear holocaust. The Korean War gave the United States and its United Nations allies a hard time, and provided the impetus for the rebuilding of the American armed forces.

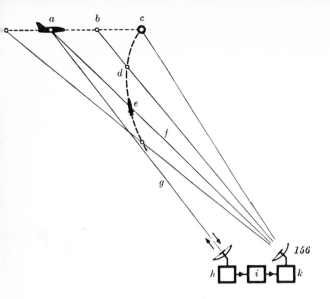

156

Generally it was fought with the arms of World War II, though the helicopter came into its own, modern nylon body armor was introduced, and jet planes first entered into extensive combat. Guerilla fighting was also a feature of the war, the North Koreans dispersing into guerilla forces when attacked. Indeed guerilla warfare, with a long history dating back to the Spanish harassment of Napoleon's troops, had become a feature of the postwar world—in Greece, Malaya, Indo-China, and China. Mao Tse-tung's classic treatise of 1937 gave the spirit of guerilla fighting in these terms: ". . . avoid the solid, attack the hollow; attack; withdraw; deliver a lightning blow, seek a lightning decision . . . harass him [the enemy] when he stops, strike him when he is weary; pursue him when he withdraws." Although the regular armies of France, England, and the United States were forced to make adjustments on the spot to the requirements of guerilla warfare, it was not until very recent times that the western nations began specifically to plan and train for this unorthodox type of fighting.

In the meantime there was the nuclear threat hanging over the world. While the United States in the early postwar era relied upon its fleet of B-36 heavy bombers to deliver the atom bomb, and later upon a larger fleet of eight-jet B-52's, there was an obvious need to develop a rocket missile along the lines of the V-2, which could deliver the bomb as a warhead without the danger of interception. Studies for an intercontinental ballistic missile (ICBM) began as early as 1946, but proceeded slowly, until the Korean War and the successful explosion of a hydrogen device in 1945 put

urgency into the program. The Russians achieved success with the fusion (hydrogen) explosion about the same time, and continued to develop their own massive ICBM, reportedly about 100 feet tall and in many stages, to deliver a tremendous hydrogen warhead halfway around the world. The brute power of this rocket was demonstrated in 1957 when the first Sputniks went up (Sputnik II, carrying the dog, Laika, weighed 1,120 pounds).

Ironically, the first American ICBM, the Atlas (which was rushed into a crash program in 1954 and made its first successful flight in 1957) was much less powerful, because, again in 1954, in a thermonuclear breakthrough, the Americans had learned how to scale down the size of the hydrogen warhead. Somewhat later than the Atlas an alternate ICBM—the more sophisticated, two-stage Titan—began to be developed; and while these huge missiles were undergoing their intricate test programs, two simpler, intermediate range (IRBM) missiles —the Thor and Jupiter—were prepared and many of them placed overseas as interim protection. The Russians had also developed a series of IRBM's which were produced in quantity, especially the two-stage, 1,800-mile range T-2 or M-103. The Atlas, operational by 1959, now delivers a 389,000 pound thrust and has a range of over 8,000 miles. Presumably the principal Russian ICBM, the T-3A, has a slightly shorter range but much more thrust and can carry a far larger warhead.

In fact the balance of terror between Russia and the United States now comes down to a relatively few Russian ICBM's delivering an enormous punch, arrayed against a far larger

157

154 (Previous page.)
The American Atlas-Able, an
intercontinental missile with
three more stages superimposed
to increase power. Atlas was first
of American big missiles,
now has 389,000 pounds of thrust
from three liquid-propellant
engines, has a range of over
9,000 miles.
155 (Previous page.) Titan I,
America's second intercontinental
missile, emerges from
underground "silo."
156 Diagram of Swiss Oerlikon
guided missile intercepting
enemy plane by means of radar.
157 Diagram showing hypothetical
application of laws of
ballistics to astronautics.

number and variety of American missiles with much smaller warheads. The once much-talked-of "missile gap" no longer exists, if it ever did. For the Americans have now gone into a "second generation" group of missiles, many of them solid—instead of liquid—pro-pellant, such as the 6,300-mile range Minute-man, or the 1,200 to 3,500-mile range Polaris, 16 of which can be fired from a single submerged nuclear-powered submarine. The mobile Polaris weapon system is probably the most strike-proof yet devised (it is thought that the Russians will soon have a similar system), while the Minuteman, protected by and launched from an underground "silo," can be fired in 30 seconds—once the 15-minute alert for an incoming enemy missile is given. The Atlas and Titan have also gone underground, as well as the new, two-stage Titan II, the most powerful of American ICBM's, now in its test program.

The Titan II, carrying a ten-megaton war-head, has a total thrust of 530,000 pounds. Using new, hypergolic fuels, it too can be launched almost immediately, Although the Polaris system will probably eventually doom the huge and vulnerable aircraft carriers of the nuclear-propelled *Enterprise* type, the United States clings to its fleet of B-52 bombers, for they can still deliver a 20-megaton bomb compared to the 5-megaton warhead of the average American ICBM. The Russian ICBM carries a warhead of well over 25 megatons. Moreover, the B-52's are now being armed with the Skybolt, a small ballistic missile hung under the wings that can be fired from the air.

While Russia has a variety of smaller rocket missiles, the United States has developed an even larger assortment of small missiles for a variety of purposes, many of them solid-propellant and with nuclear capability. One of the first of the tactical, "battlefield" missiles was the Honest John of 1954, a shortrange ballistic missile that can carry an atomic warhead. The later Davey Crockett atomic mortar has a range of about six miles, a minimal blast, and can be used at the battalion or even company level. Among larger tactical missiles, the solid-propellant Sergeant and Pershing are replacing the older Corporal and Redstone. There are many air-to-air rocket missiles like the Sidewinder and Falcon weapon systems, and a variety of antiaircraft missiles such as the Hawk or Nike Hercules, the latter grouped in bases. Finally, naval ships are armed with the solid-propellant, ship-to-shore Terrier and smaller Tartar, replacing ship-based artillery.

Radar, used in a variety of ways, from the huge, complex early-warning nets against plane or missile attack to tiny compact sets for detect-ing men or vehicles in darkness or fog, has become almost a weapon in itself. The early-warning systems, designed to detect incoming bombers, now team intercepting missiles with planes, and are barely adequate to warn against incoming ICBM's. For the future, the American Midas and Samos satellite systems may take their place, the one detecting ICBM launchings with an infrared heat-sensing system, the other photographing enemy installations from orbit. Then of course there is always the possibility of what the space fiction writers like to call "war in the skies"—but at present satellites armed with hydrogen bombs would seem to be far too vulnerable. There is nothing that such

95

159

160   Bullet-riddled automobile
in which Trujillo, dictator
of Dominican Republic,
met his death. Sudden social
upheavals, revolutions,
coups d'état or long-drawn-out
guerilla wars, rather than large-scale
formal wars, have become typical
of the modern era, necessitating
a reorientation in the objectives
and equipment of modern armies
and police forces.
161   Such a sudden social
upheaval was the tragic
Hungarian uprising late in 1956.
Hungarian insurgent on streets
of Budapest wields Russian DP
light machine gun.

161

162 Swiss soldier on maneuvers
carries the bazooka and the
Swiss-made anti-tank "tromblon."
Rocket projectiles for the weapon
are carried on soldier's backs.
In an old and honored tradition,
Swiss still have a "citizen army"
in which every able-bodied
male must serve.
163 During standard
infantry training another Swiss
soldier in camouflage uniform
leans his new Swiss-made,
1957 model assault rifle
against tank. Tank is probably
British-made, since smaller
nations often buy foreign-made
heavier arms.

163

164   The Tartar, a ship-based,
solid-propellant rocket missile.
Many American warships are now
armed with the Tartar and its
bigger brother, the Terrier.
Since World War II rockets of
all sizes and for many different
missions have been developed,
including such tactical field weapons
as the Honest John and Lacrosse,
the airborne Sidewinder and
Falcon, and the Hawk or
Nike Hercules anti-aircraft
systems.
165   But the decisive weapon
of our time in determining strategy
is the dread intercontinental
missile. Here an Atlas rises
from its pad.

165

a system could do that is not already done better by the intercontinental missile. As for developments in chemical and biological warfare, no information is available. Both are certainly being studied, but one hopes that the informal ban on their use will continue into the future.

Compared to such considerations there has been very little change since World War II in conventional weapons. The trend in small arms has been toward replacing several weapons with one, the new American M-14 rifle, for instance, replacing the M-1 rifle, M-2 carbine, "grease gun" submachine gun, and Browning Automatic Rifle. Submachine guns are becoming more popular as guerilla warfare increases (typical is the 9-pound, 25-round Israeli Uzi). In most countries the new assault rifles have been made so flexible that the distinction between assault rifle and light machine gun is rapidly disappearing. In artillery, the new American self-propelled 175 mm gun, capable of firing either conventional or nuclear projectiles, brings the United States up to the high standards hitherto set by the Soviet Union. Sporting weapons tend to follow military styles, but favor the stronger bolt action, or lever and pump actions, rather than automatic actions, which are considered too dangerous.

But all in all, when compared with the new rocket and nuclear weapons, these are trifling changes. Yet at the same time they are important, for guerilla and limited warfare, using primarily conventional weapons, begins to grow in significance as the nuclear stalemate, even though precariously, is maintained from year to year.

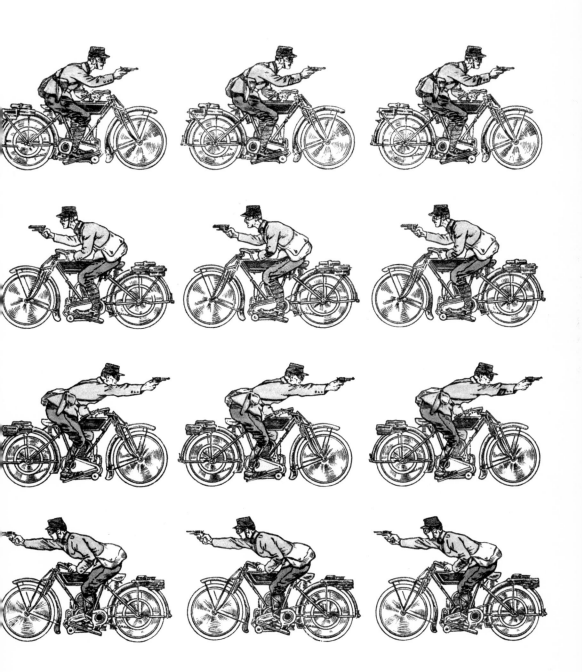

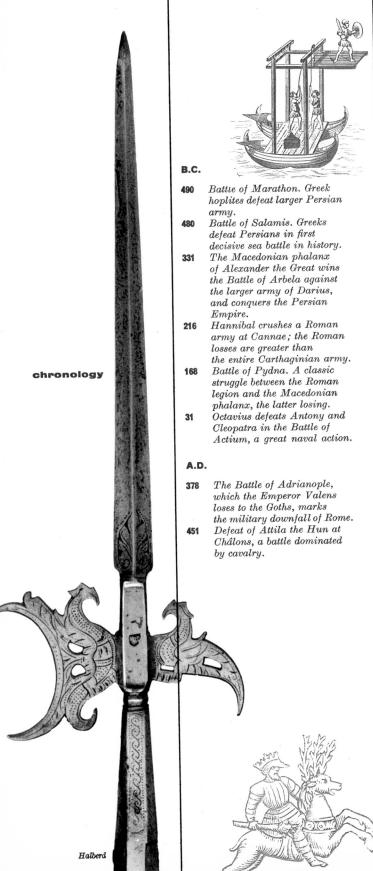

Roman boat for sea-attack on forts

chronology

B.C.

490 Battle of Marathon. Greek hoplites defeat larger Persian army.

480 Battle of Salamis. Greeks defeat Persians in first decisive sea battle in history.

331 The Macedonian phalanx of Alexander the Great wins the Battle of Arbela against the larger army of Darius, and conquers the Persian Empire.

216 Hannibal crushes a Roman army at Cannae; the Roman losses are greater than the entire Carthaginian army.

168 Battle of Pydna. A classic struggle between the Roman legion and the Macedonian phalanx, the latter losing.

31 Octavius defeats Antony and Cleopatra in the Battle of Actium, a great naval action.

A.D.

378 The Battle of Adrianople, which the Emperor Valens loses to the Goths, marks the military downfall of Rome.

451 Defeat of Attila the Hun at Châlons, a battle dominated by cavalry.

Halberd

717 Saracens lay siege to Constantinople, are beaten off. For centuries thereafter the Byzantine Empire holds off the Arabs from Europe.

886 Vikings attack Paris, are driven off.

1066 Norman invader, William the Conqueror, defeats Harold of England at the Battle of Hastings.

1187 Battle of Hattin (or Tiberias), in which the crusaders are defeated by the Saracens under Saladin.

1204 The crusaders take Constantinople, burning and looting the city.

1220 Genghis Khan conquers the great Khwarismian Empire in Persia, in five months. The Mongolian hordes of horsemen were reinforced by Chinese technicians, highly skilled in the art of

Helmet, sixteenth century

siegecraft, whom the Great Khan had assimilated into his army when he invaded China in 1211.

1241 Mongols invade Europe, penetrating as far as Poland and the Adriatic before returning to Asia.

1249 English monk Roger Bacon records a formula for gunpowder (black powder)— made of saltpeter, charcoal, and sulphur.

1302 Battle of Courtrai. The cream of French chivalry is defeated by the Flemish infantry.

1324 First documentary evidence of the use of cannon, at the siege of Metz.

1346 English longbowmen defeat French cavalry at the Battle of Crécy.

1396 The Swiss pikemen, grouped in a phalanx, defend their country against the Austrians, at Sempach, near Lucerne.

1400 Approximate date for the invention of the matchlock.

Northern king on reindeer, Middle Ages

Grenade *Self-propelled fire bomb*

Elaborate sixteenth century armor

Siege method

Hussite Wars. Bohemian rebel, Jan Zizka makes efficient tactical use of a combination of cavalry, infantry, and artillery. The decisive battle of the closing years of the Hundred Years' War is won by the French at Formigny. Constantinople falls to the Turks. Their siege artillery breaks down the most formidable system of fortifications in Europe. French artillery ends the legend of Swiss invincibility, at the Battle of Marignano. Invention of the wheellock, a firearm mechanism in which the charge is ignited by sparks from a spinning, serated wheel acting on pyrites. Invention of the snaphaunce, an early Dutch flintlock with a manually operated pan cover. Battle of Pavia, the decisive battle of the Italian Wars. The Spanish arquebusiers of Charles V rout the pike-men of the French. Invention of the miquelet, an early Spanish flintlock. The musket was also invented at about this time. Basically a larger version of the arquebus, the musket, used with a portable rest, was able to double the range and load of the arquebus.

1571 Battle of Lepanto. Christian forces defeat Moslems in this decisive naval engagement.

1588 The English defeat the Spanish Armada.

1618- Thirty Years' War, a period
1640 of brutality, looting, and plundering throughout Europe.

1630 Introduction of the flintlock, a firearm mechanism employing flint against steel for ignition. Widely used until early in the nineteenth century.

1666 The Marquis of Louvois becomes minister of war under Louis XIV, reorganiz- ing the French army. Soldiers, equipped with flintlocks and bayonets, are trained in linear maneuvers.

1673 At the siege of Maestricht, military engineer Sébastien le Prestre de Vauban introduces a system of parallel trenches, used in siegecraft for the next 150 years.

1701- War of the Spanish Succes-
1714 sion. Such military leaders as Marlborough and Prince Eugene of Savoy lead the forces of the Great Alliance against those of Louis XIV.

1745 Battle of Fontenoy, during the War of the Austrian Succession, is one of the classic battles employing linear tactics. Led by Marshal Saxe, the French defeat the forces of the Dutch, British, and Hanoverians.

1757 Battle of Leuthen, won by the "big guns" and "oblique order" (the battalions moving forward in a diagonal line) of Frederick the Great, during the Seven Years' War.

1759 During the French and Indian War (the Seven Years' War in Europe), both British General Wolfe and French General Montcalm lose their lives at the Battle of Quebec, which was decided by the deadly fire of the line of British musketeers.

1777 The rifle, with spirally-grooved barrel, used by the American

Paré's wooden leg

American Indians, de Bry

Tilting helmet

frontiersmen during the
American Revolution, wins
a victory over smoothbore
muskets of the British, at
Saratoga.

1793 The French Committee of
Public Safety decrees universal conscription, the "levée
en masse."

1796 General Napoleon Bonaparte
wins his first campaign in
Italy.

1805 British Admiral Horatio
Nelson loses his life while
winning his greatest victory,
at Trafalgar.

1805 Battle of Austerlitz, the peak
of Napoleon's career.

1807 Napoleon invades Prussia,
defeating rigidly-trained
Prussian soldiers (the Prussians still clung to linear
tactics) in the battles of
Jena and Auerstedt.

1807 Massed French artillery
defeats the Russian army at
Friedland.

1807 Dr. Alexander Forsyth, a
Scottish minister, patents
a percussion lock.

1812 Napoleon invades Russia in
June, retreats from Moscow
in October, leaving the

disintegrating "Grande
Armée" behind him.

1815 Having abdicated in 1814,
Napoleon attempts a come-
back in the Hundred Days
(March 1-June 18). He is
defeated by Wellington at
Waterloo.

1835 Samuel Colt receives
the first patent on a cap-and-
ball revolver.

1835 French gunmaker Flobert
begins work on a rim-fire
cartridge.

1836 Parisian gunsmith E. Lefaucheux develops the pin-fire
cartridge.

1837 The British Army adopts
percussion-firing
muskets.

1838 The first successful breechloading rifle (loading through
the rear of the barrel),
the Prussian Dreyse Needle
Gun is developed.

1851 The British army adopts
rifles using the Minié ball,
invented by Captain Charles
Minié of the French army
in 1849.

1855 During the Crimean War,
English nurse Florence
Nightingale succeeds in

establishing proper medical
treatment for the wounded.

1857 Smith and Wesson produce
the first metallic cartridge
revolver.

1859 Battle of Solferino. The rifled,
breechloading fieldpieces used
by Napoleon III won this
victory over the Austrians.

1860 The first successful repeating
rifle is invented by 20-year-
old Christopher Spencer and
tested by President Lincoln.

1861 F.E. Schneider of Paris
takes out a patent, in
England, on first widely used
center-fire cartridge.

1861- The American Civil War sees
1865 the use of breechloading
cannon, the Minié ball,
repeating rifles.

1862 Dr. Richard Gatling invents
the first practical machine gun.

1864 Foundation of the International Red Cross, by
Henri Dunant, at Geneva.

1867 The first bolt-action, repeating
rifle is developed by the Swiss,
Frederic Vetterli.

1867- During the Franco-Prussian
1871 War, the French use
the machine gun for the first
time in Europe.

German hunting gun, c. 1630

Trajectory of a mortar

4 In England, Hiram Maxim develops the first automatic machine gun, operating by recoil.

4 Development of smokeless powder (with a nitro-cellulose base), in France.

9 American gunsmith John M. Browning starts experimentation on what is to be his first successful gas-operated machine gun.

2 The Hotchkiss Company produces the first version of their successful gas-piston-operated machine gun.

3 First widely used semi-automatic pistol, designed by the American Hugo Borchardt and produced in Germany. Ancestor of the Luger.

9- The South African (Boer)
2 War, marked by the use of smokeless powder, repeating rifles, protective coloring in clothing, and campaigns which relied on mobility and surprise.

4- Russo-Japanese War. First
5 full-scale use of machine guns, field telephones, and radios. "Big gun" naval battles,

the use of mines and torpedoes also typified this war.

1914- World War I. First use of
1918 tanks and poison gas. Massive artillery barrages, widespread use of machine guns, aerial bombing directed at civilians, and the destruction of enemy resources also characterized the war. Camouflage was widely used, and soldiers were issued steel helmets, the first "armor" of recent times.

1914 Battle of the Marne. Motorized transport, the telephone, and aerial observation played a great part in winning this Allied victory (one French division was driven to the front in Parisian taxicabs).

1914 Trench warfare begins late in the fall as mobility is reduced on both sides.

1914 First aerial bombing of the war, as German Zeppelin dirigibles bomb English civilians on Christmas Eve.

1915 Germans release chlorine gas, the first poison gas attack in history, causing 70,000 Allied casualties in three weeks, at Ypres.

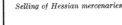

ench hussar, Napoleonic wars

Ottoman artillery, eighteenth century

Selling of Hessian mercenaries

Greek guerilla soldier

American M-60 machine gun

Police trainin

1916 Tanks go into action for the first time as British Mark I's make a rather unsuccessful attack on German positions in the Somme region, September 15.

1917 Tanks are reintroduced into the war by the British and prove their merit as an armored attack on Cambrai breaks through the Hindenburg line.

1918 Allied offensives against the Soissons-Rheims, Amiens, and Saint-Mihiel salients force evacuation of these areas by the Germans.

1936 Outbreak of the Spanish Civil War, during which Germany tested its new military planes and blitzkrieg tactics. July 13.

1939- 1945 World War II. Characterized by extensive use of automatic fire, using semi- and fully automatic weapons such as the submachine gun and the machine rifle, as well as improved tanks and artillery. New weapons included flame-throwers, rockets, the VT (proximity) fuse, the atom bomb.

1939 Poland crushed by Nazi blitzkrieg.

1940 Germans overrun Holland, Belgium, and France in May and June. In the Battle of Britain, August 8-October 30, the British Royal Air Force wards off invasion in an aerial bout with the Luftwaffe.

1941 Crete falls to the Germans after the first large-scale airborne invasion in history, May 20-29.

1941 Nazi invasion of Russia, June 22.

1941 Japanese carrier-borne planes attack the American bases at Pearl Harbor and in the Philippines, December 7.

1942 Battles of the Coral Sea (May 7-8) and Midway (June 3-7) in which, for the first time, aircraft carriers play a major role on both sides, halting the Japanese advance.

1942 First major turning point of the war, as the Allied forces win strategic battles all over the globe during the "twenty days of November": British defeat General Rommel in North Africa, November 1-3; invasion of North Africa, by Anglo-American forces, November 8; Japanese invasion of Guadalcanal beaten off, November 13-15; Russians surround German army at Stalingrad, November 19.

1943 Allied offensive marks the second turning point in the war in the "twenty days of July": Americans land in the Solomons, July 1-5; Sicily invaded by Anglo-American forces, July 10; Russian army nullifies German summer offensive, July 13-20.

1944 "The twenty days of June," third great turning point in the war: Anglo-American forces take Rome, June 4; D-Day invasion of Normandy, June 6; strategic bombing of Japan begins, June 16; Americans win naval battle of the Philippine Sea, June 18; Soviet summer offensive begins, June 23.

1944 Germans fire first V-2 rockets against Paris, September 6. London is attacked by V-2s two days later.

1944 Paris falls to the Allied forces, August 25.

1944 First bombing of Tokyo by land-based planes, November 24.

1944 Battle of the Bulge, December 16-25. Using King Tiger tanks, machine pistols, and the 88-mm gun, the Germans advance 50 miles into the Allied lines in the Ardennes before being stopped.

1945 Atomic bombs dropped on Hiroshima, August 6, and Nagasaki, August 9.

1947- 1954 Guerilla war in Indo-China between Communist Vietminh and France.

1949 Formation of the North Atlantic Treaty Organization (NATO), March 17.

1950- 1953 Korean War. Largest use to date of massive firepower, with enormous ammunition expenditures. Close combat, trench warfare, widespread use of helicopters, adoption of nylon and Fiberglas armor vests also typified the war

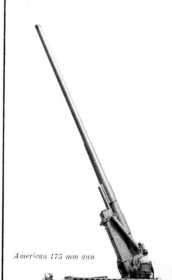

American 175 mm gun

Antiaircraft cannon

*Among those who have assisted in the
preparation of this book grateful
acknowledgment must be made to
Helen Muller and Eric Tschumi of the
ENI staff, as well as to the
Musée d'Art et d'Histoire, Geneva,
and to Robert Teichmann, New York.
Documentation: Nicolas Bouvier, David Kronig.*

credits

*Ansco Historical Collection,
Photo Mathew Brady: 131.
Archives Photographiques: 3, 5.
Bibliothèque de Genève: 109;
7, "Bataille de Kadesh" (Breasted);
84, 89, 90, "De Pe Militari"
(Valturius 1534); 83, 85, 86, 88, 91-94,
"De Re Militari" (Vegetius 1535);
100, 115, "Artillerie..." (Ufano 1621);
141, "Nouvelles Armes..." (Schmidt).
Bibliothèque Nationale, Paris:
1, "Les Rues de Pékin"; 17, 20-26,
(Byzantine Manuscript 10th century);
38, "Maniement d'armes" (Gheyn 1618);
27-29, 97, 98, 101-108, 116-118, 130, 135-7, 149.
Bibliothèque du Musée de l'Artillerie, Paris:
110-114.
British Museum, London: 4.
Collection Nicolas Bouvier: 30, 31, 35-37.
Collection Charles Dollfus: 127-129,
133, 134, 138, 139, 142.
Collection Huguenin: 10, 11, 14, 15, 18, 19.
Collection Kappeler: 140, 143, 144.
Collection Pierre Pasquier: 166.
Comet: 162, 163.
Deutsches Museum, Munich: 87, 95, 96, 124-126.
Douglas Aircraft: 151.
Dumont: 146.
Firma Fried. Krupp: 145.
Frederic Lewis: 147.
General Dynamics (Convair): 154, 164, 165.
Giraudon: 9, 12, 13, 16, 32-34, 99.
Held: 8.
Hispano Suiza: 152.
L'Illustration, 1871: 123.
Interavia: 155.
Library of Congress, Photo Mathew Brady: 132.
Life: 158.
Magnum: Photo Andrew Saint George, 160.
Photo Eric Lessing, 161.
Musée d'Art et d'Histoire, Geneva:
40-81, 119-122.
Musée des Invalides, Paris: 2, 39, 82.
Musée du Louvre, Paris: 6.
Private Collection: 148.
Que Sais-je?, "L'Astronautique": 157.
"Raketentechnik," Stuttgart, 1958: 153, 156.
Rapho: 159.
USAF: 150.*

Chronology

*Archives Photographiques: 12.
Bibliothek der E.T.H., Zurich: 5.
Bibliothèque de Genève: 15, 18.
Bibliothèque Nationale, Paris: 3, 9, 10, 13, 16, 19.
Collection Charles Dollfus: 6.
Collection Kappeler: 2.
Giraudon: 8, 14.
Musée de Genève: 1.
Musée des Invalides, Paris: 4, 7, 11.
NATO: 20, 21, 25-27.
Rapho: 17.
Stoeger Arms Corporation: 23.
U.S. Army: 22, 24.*

NATO soldier in training

Printed in Switzerland